QE NURSE 1938–1957

CLARENCE HOUSE
S.W. 1

I offer my congratulations to the members of the Queen Elizabeth Hospital Nurses League on their initiative in producing a history of nurse training at the Hospital in the years from 1938 to 1957.

The book recalls memories of those who took their first steps as student nurses and the experienced nurses who guided their education and training during the early years of the new hospital.   There will also be much to interest past patients and staff who have had associations with the hospital and its development.

I send to you all my best wishes for the future and I pray for the continuance of your dedicated work to foster the spirit of friendship among Nurses.

ELIZABETH R
Queen Mother

1997

QE NURSE 1938–1957

A history of nursing at the Queen Elizabeth Hospital, Birmingham

Edited by
Collette Clifford

Compiled by
Doreen Tennant
Jeffrey Wood
Ann-Carol Carrington

BREWIN BOOKS

First published by
Brewin Books, Studley, Warwickshire, B80 7LG
in May 1997

ISBN: 1 85858 097 8

British Library in Cataloguing in Publication Data.
A Catalogue record for this book is available from the British Library

Typeset by Avon Dataset Ltd, Bidford on Avon, B50 4JH
Printed by Warwick Printing Co Ltd. Warwick

Acknowledgements

Members of the Queen Elizabeth Hospital Nurses League (QEHNL), initiated the idea of developing this book and also provided the financial support to launch the project and for that we are very grateful. The processes involved in developing this book are described in the Preface where it will be noted that the production of this book relied on the help and goodwill of a range of people listed overleaf.

The Special Trustees for the former United Birmingham Hospitals Trust Funds provided funds to support the development of this project. In particular we would like to thank Mr R. C. Blythin, Secretary to the Special Trustees for his advice during the preparation of this book.

The editors of QEHNL Magazine gave permission to publish extracts in this text. In addition we have used a number of pictures and other illustrations and sources of these are acknowledged in the text as appropriate. A number of photographs were taken from Hospital archives. However, we would like to note that a large number of people kindly provided photographs and other memorabilia that we were unable to use because of lack of space, but we would like to thank these for their support.

The compiling and editing of this material was a big task and for this we would like to acknowledge the help given by Mrs Pam Techene for typing in the early days of the project and, in the later stages, to Miss Margaret Webster who also undertook the final proof reading of the manuscript.

The Queen Elizabeth Hospital is now part of the University Hospital Birmingham NHS Trust and our final thanks go to the Trust for allowing us to prepare and publish this book. In particular we would like to acknowledge Mrs Sharon Goodman the present Director of Nursing and Quality in the Trust, without whose support it would not have been possible to produce this text.

Glossary of abbreviations
QEH = Queen Elizabeth Hospital
QEHNTS = Queen Elizabeth Hospital Nurse Training School (1938–1957)
PTS = Preliminary Training School
QESN = Queen Elizabeth School of Nursing (1957–1989)
QEHNL = Queen Elizabeth Hospital Nurses League

Steering Group (listed in alphabetical order)

Ann-Carol Carrington   QEHNTS   47th PTS
Collette Clifford   Professor of Nursing, University of Birmingham
Sheila Garlick   QEHNTS   47th PTS
Maggie Griffiths   Senior Nurse, University Hospital NHS Trust, Birmingham
Peter Nolan   Lecturer in Nursing/Nurse Historian, University of Birmingham
Doreen Tennant   QEHNTS   19th PTS
John Jeffrey Wood   QEHNTS   25th PTS
Marian Wood   QEHNTS   58th PTS

The interviewers (listed in alphabetical order)

Sylvia Davies
Rhona Griffiths
Jeanette Griffiths
Margaret Rich
Kathleen Spragg
Doreen Tennant
Dorothy Wood
Marian Wood
John Jeffrey Wood

People interviewed for this project

Queens Hospital Nurses
Miss Margaret Birch
Mrs Barbara Quinton (nee Stephens)
Miss Muriel Taylor

Members of Queen Elizabeth Hospital Nurses League listed by Preliminary Training School (PTS) number as appropriate

Grace Emery (nee Hufton)	1st	Isabelle Houghton (nee Kitson)	31st
Edna Cooper (nee Stanley)	2nd	Cynthia Bolton (nee Haughton)	32nd
Jennie Starr-Martin (nee Walker)	3rd	Harriet Faulkner (nee Edwards)	39th
Dawn Hayes (nee Weston)	4th	Margaret Sykes (nee Brereton)	41st
Dorothy Ramsden*	4th	Jean Clarke (nee Goodall)	43rd
Cathleen Elliott (Dr)	5th	Margaret Stone (nee Weymouth)	45th
Barbara Weaver (nee Astles)	5th	Shirley Hughs (nee Johnson)	53rd
Jean Dawson-Edwards (nee Button)	7th	Nancy Meades (nee Moore)	55th
Winifred Hill (nee Wagstaff)	10th	Deborah Moriaty (nee Peake)	56th
Margaret Moody (nee Barnacle)	10th	Susan Hardwick (nee Mottram)	57th
Ursula Smyth (nee Mindelsohn)	10th	Anne Wood (nee Bulmer)	60th
Sheila Mistygacz (nee Gore)	13th	Judith Standley (nee Kendon)	64th
Ursula Rooker (nee Durkin)	13th	Jennifer Bayliss (nee Byworth)	66th
Doreen Tennant	19th	Angela Pickles (nee Probyn-Skinner)	68th
Mary Dalton (nee Wood)	24th	Edith Thould	
Margaret Clews	21st	*Other Contributing memories*	
Monica Stiff (nee Flowers)*	25th	Floyd S. Barringer MD*	
Betty Pugh	27th	Paul Dawson Edwards FRCS	
Marion Reed	30th		

* now deceased

Contents

Preface

This book describes the history of some of the nurses who trained and worked in the Queen Elizabeth Hospital (QEH), Birmingham. The hospital opened to the public in 1938 and over many years the hospital has served, not only to care for those in need, but to take a lead role in the education and training of a range of health care professionals, the largest group of which is nurses.

Nurse training began at the QEH even before it opened, as tutorial staff worked to prepare student nurses to care for patients in the new hospital. That experience of nurse training was seen as unique by the nurses who had the opportunity to work in a new, purpose built hospital during the early years. This book will focus on those experiences. This history is definitive only in as much as it covers the period 1938–1957, this being the life span of the Queen Elizabeth Hospital Nurse Training School (QEHNTS).

Nurses who completed their training in that school, and those who worked in the QEH, during the time span identified, formed a League, the Queen Elizabeth Hospital Nurses League (QEHNL), that continues to thrive today. It is to the Queen Elizabeth Hospital Nurses League that credit for the book must be given for it would not have been developed without the interest and support of members.

The format of the book

This book tracks the development of nursing at the QEH starting with a background chapter outlining the experience of nursing in other hospitals in the city from which some of the staff for the new QEH were drawn. This is followed by an account of the development of the QEH and the nurses home to set the scene for the nurse memories that follow. A chapter is dedicated to the training programme and specific memories associated with the rules and regulations of the day as the student nurses worked to become registered nurses.

The hospital itself opened just before the outbreak of war and a chapter is given over to the experiences at that time. This is followed by an account of memories of the peace time conditions up to the late 1950's. The last two chapters focus on two smaller groups of nursing staff in the QEH. The experience of the male nurse, a new innovation in the early years of the QEH, is considered. This is followed by an account of some of the leaders in nursing who made an impact on nursing at the QEH and the wider nursing community.

The experiences outlined in this book will be of interest to all those nurses who are curious about the origins of their practice. At a local level this history will have personal relevance for all those who have worked in the hospital, lived in the locality, or been a patient or a relative who has visited the QEH. The experiences reported here will also, no doubt, stir up memories for others who worked in similar environments in years gone by. In addition the text may be of appeal to those who are interested in local history. This book offers a snapshot of working life for one group of people and so contributes to a wider understanding of the social history of the city in which it is set. Furthermore, the approach used to develop an 'oral history' project represents a potential way forward for nurses or other health care workers to consider ways in which they could develop research into local history.

Developing the project
This study was co-ordinated by a steering group listed at the beginning of this book, who remained active throughout in supporting the development of this project. It should perhaps also be noted at the outset that the meetings of the steering group would have provided enough information for a book! The first meetings of the group were quite focused on developing the project. Once this moved beyond the technicalities to the experiences of the steering group members, the 'trips down memory lane' demonstrated the vast wealth of historical information held in the minds of ex QEH nurses. This demonstrated the value of the oral history method in providing information for this text but it is to the regret of the editor that the steering group meetings were not themselves tape recorded for they would have provided a companion volume for this text! Consequently we advise any other groups undertaking a similar project to have the tape recorder ready at steering group meetings.

The initial framework for collecting information proposed that a group of volunteers would take responsibility for interviewing a number of nurses who had trained and worked in the QEH in the time specified above. The steering group needed to consider how they would identify, firstly, those nurses who would do the interviews and secondly, those who would be interviewed.

Finding the interviewers was not a problem as a number of QEHNL members expressed a willingness to help with this and to these people, listed in the acknowledgements section we are very grateful. The choice of people to be interviewed was based on a number of factors, one of which was to ensure that a range of experiences across the years of the existence of the QEHNTS were reflected in the information collected. Each student nurse entering this school joined a group identified by a 'set number'. The first group starting in 1938 was set number 1 and the last, entering in 1957 was set number 68 giving a total 68 sets of nurses, all of whom are entitled to membership of the QEHNL. To get a reasonable representation of experience over the 20 year span (1938–57) covered by this project it was decided to identify a couple of potential participants from each set who were members of the QEHNL and therefore accessible to the project team as their location was known through league records. The next step was to identify people had had joined the QEHNL by rights gained by working as members of the nursing staff in the QEH over the same time period.

Key figures from this group were drawn from the list of League members. Finally, because of the links with the Queen's Hospital (see Chapter 1), efforts were made to gather the memories of nurses who had worked in that hospital before services were transferred to the QEH.

The end result of this exercise was the production of 34 tape recorded interviews with nurses who had trained or worked in the QEH over the time period described in the text. The tape recorded interviews were transcribed and summarised and at this stage credit must be given to Miss Doreen Tennant who painstakingly listened to all the interviews and transcribed them in great detail to give the basis for much of the material in this book. This was no mean feat as simply listening to each tape represented a major time investment. This was followed by a thematic approach in data analysis drawing out issues outlined in this book. The process involved in this is very time consuming and demands a great deal of effort on the part of the analyst and consequently it is very important that this work be acknowledged as a major contribution to the book.

In the course of the study we were very aware of the need to ensure the anonymity of people responding to our request for information. The editorial team decided that to preserve anonymity we would avoid identifying individual nurses who were interviewed by name. However, credit should be give to all those who participated so willingly in the interviews and their help is acknowledged in earlier pages of this book.

We were very encouraged by the willingness of people to share their memorabilia with us as demonstrated by the range of photographs and other material included in the text. As noted earlier, there was far more available to us than we could use in a text of this size and so we are hoping others will rise to the challenge of using this material and complete a follow up text.

From this perspective acknowledgement must be give to members of the steering group who scoured local records available in the archives and libraries and here special note is given to the work completed by Jeffrey Wood, who spent many hours in the local libraries drawing on hospital records that have provided a lot of information in this book, again another time consuming exercise. Also the efforts of Ann-Carol Carrington and Sheila Garlick in searching records must be acknowledged as this was much appreciated.

The finally acknowledgement goes to other members of the Steering Group, particularly Maggie Griffiths and Peter Nolan who contributed much to the debate in developing this book and undertook to read and comment on the final draft of the manuscript.

The book will be published just one year before the Queen Elizabeth Hospital, Birmingham celebrates its Diamond Jubilee. Consequently it is anticipated that the information contained in the following pages will serve as an appropriate tribute to those nurses who gave so much of their lives to the hospital in the early years.

Chapter 1

Influences Prior to 1938

The Queen Elizabeth Hospital (QEH), Birmingham opened to the public in 1938. However, the story of nursing in the QEH, begins many years before as the model of nursing that developed could be traced to nurses working in other hospitals in the City, for, as will seen later, a number moved to work in the new hospital when it opened.

Before 1938 there were a number of hospitals in the City of Birmingham. Of these a group of hospitals were known as voluntary hospitals, that is hospitals supported by public subscription. These included the General Hospital Birmingham, the Queen's Hospital Birmingham, the Midland Nerve Hospital and the King Edward VII Children's Hospital. Other hospitals such as those at Selly Oak and Dudley Road and the Fever Hospital in the east of the City, were funded by the City.

Out of these the Queen's Hospital, Birmingham is generally seen as the precursor to the Queen Elizabeth Hospital as the services and many of the staff moved from here when the new Centre Hospital, later to become known as the Queen Elizabeth Hospital, opened.

The Queen's Hospital
The Queen's Hospital was founded in 1841 primarily for the purpose of clinical instruction of Queen's College medical students. Prior to that date the General Hospital, Birmingham had been used for that purpose but growth in the number of medical students meant there was a need for more clinical facilities. As such it was the first teaching hospital in the UK for which education was a fundamental founding purpose, although the growth of the town and the population and the associated need for health care were also major considerations.

As a hospital in the old voluntary sector there was a need to consider the ways in which the public could contribute towards the funds to support the hospital, and the local community was very active in raising the funds necessary to support other voluntary hospitals such as the General Hospital in the centre of Birmingham.

Another source of funding developed a little later in 1873 was the

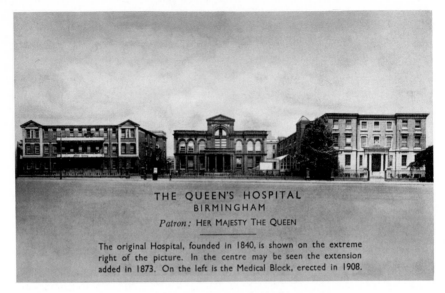

THE QUEEN'S HOSPITAL
BIRMINGHAM
Patron: HER MAJESTY THE QUEEN

The original Hospital, founded in 1840, is shown on the extreme right of the picture. In the centre may be seen the extension added in 1873. On the left is the Medical Block, erected in 1908.

Queens Hospital 1841.

The General Hospital, 1925.

Birmingham Hospital Saturday Fund. This was founded by Joseph Sampson Gamgee who was a remarkable man. He was born in Italy and first qualified as a Veterinary Surgeon, only later becoming a Surgeon in the new Queen's Hospital. He invented a special dressing known as Gamgee Tissue and the disposable sanitary towel and so his name lived on as many generations of nurses continued to use the Gamgee tissue in wound dressings.

At that time the churches in the City nominated one Sunday each year to raise money for the local hospitals and Joseph Gamgee wondered if a similar scheme could raise funds to build an Outpatient department at the Queen's Hospital. He proposed at a meeting that the City's working people should donate a Saturday afternoon's overtime pay to hospital fund-raising. This idea was warmly supported and in the first year over £9000 was raised and, with street collections and other sources of funds, sufficient money was raised to build the Outpatient extension. So the Birmingham Hospital Saturday Fund, was born and continued to raise funds until the NHS arrived (QEHNL Magazine 1994). After this the fund continued although the money was redirected to the benefits of the contributors and the fund continues to support professional development through scholarships awarded to nurses today.

By the 1930's it had become apparent that the Queen's Hospital was no longer big enough to cater for the demands for care of the day and plans were made to develop a new hospital for Birmingham which later became known as the Queen Elizabeth Hospital

In due course some senior members of staff; Mr. L.E. Challice, Chief Technician in Bacteriology and Clinical Pathology, Mr. E. G. Speakman the Pharmacist, Mr G. Hurford the House Governor, Miss E. Collett the Night Superintendent and many of the 'Honoraries', today known as Consultants, and a number of ward sisters moved to the new hospital. As these nurses were to bring the standards set in their work at the Queen's hospital to the new Centre Hospital it was decided that it would be important to interview some nurses who had trained and worked at the Queen's Hospital as part of the project reported in this book, an outline of their memories is given below.

Nursing at the Queen's Hospital
In common with most hospital at that time nurses at the Queen's Hospital formed the biggest group of workers. The growth of this group is demonstrated in the history of the Hospital which notes that the Nurses Home, erected in 1887, was extended again in 1908 by which time there were 178 beds in the hospital and 74 beds in the nurses home (Barnes 1952)

The regulations governing the appointment and duties of the matron is interesting (Figure 1.1) as is the salary of the mid 19th century associated with the post (£20 per annum). The influences of the church in the Hospital at this time is also interesting as the need to ensure that all patients 'as are able' attended services in the Chapel is documented.

By the late 1800's further information was available and statistics relating to nursing in the Queen's Hospital provided another source of interest for the readers of the QEH Nurses League magazine (Figure 1.2).

From the early part of the 1900's the General Nursing Council (GNC) was the official organisation responsible for managing courses leading to the

---

Figure 1.1:
Extract from the Regulations of the Queen's Hospital – mid 19th century

"The establishment shall consist of a Chaplain, three Physicians, three Surgeons, one Assistant Physician and one Assistant Surgeon, Dispenser, Secretary, a Matron, a Collector, a Physician's Assistant and a House Surgeon".

The Matron shall not be less than 30, nor more than 50 years of age, at the time of her election: she shall reside in the Hospital and have a salary of £20 per annum, or such other salary as the Committee of Council may determine.

The Matron's duties:- She shall take care that every patient has clean sheets when admitted and that they be changed every 14 days or oftener if necessary, and whenever the weather will permit, she shall order a certain number of mattresses, blankets and quilts in rotation, to be exposed to the sun and well aired. She shall see that the private apartments of the offices of the institution be cleaned and put into proper order by 8 a.m.. She shall preside at the meals of the Resident Medical Officers and take care that the breakfast be served at 8 a.m., and dinner not later than 3 p.m. and that no meal be allowed in the private rooms of the Resident Medical Officers, except in case of sickness. She shall examine or see examined, the bundles, boxes, baskets and (if need be) that apparel of all newly admitted patients, in their presence, or in that of their friends, with a view to prevent the introduction of any improper articles. She shall see that such patients as are able, attend in the Chapel, when Divine Service is performed. The keys of all doors are to be in the keeping of the Matron, and she shall cause the doors to be locked up every evening at 9 p.m. in the winter, and at 10 p.m. in the summer.

(Reproduced from the Queen Elizabeth Hospital Nurses League magazine 1971)

Figure 1.2
The Queen's Hospital – 1899

The following article is taken from a copy of **"Burdett's Official Nursing Directory 1899"**, and will particularly interest our members who trained at the "Queens".

Birmingham Queen's Hospital 1898

Number of Beds 132

Staff:-   Lady Superintendent
           Night Superintendent
    7   Sisters
    7   Staff Nurses
    9   2nd year Probationers
    12   1st year Probationers

Applications: average 300   Vacancies: 10 yearly

Candidates must be between 23 and 33 years of age, and must produce satisfactory evidence as to character, education, health and physique. After a personal interview and 3 months trial, candidates are received for 4 years training, 2 years in hospital and 2 years either as a Staff Nurse or on the external staff.
Lectures are given by the Lady Superintendent upon nursing and elementary anatomy and physiology, and by the casualty surgeon and physician of out-patients on more advanced medical and surgical subjects. Certificates (for 3 years training) are granted at the end of the 4 year course, after satisfactorily completing the engagement and passing the examination.

Recreation:-   2 hours daily
          long pass 3–10 p.m. 1 day weekly and alternate Sundays
          2 weeks holiday in a year.
Premium:-   Nil
Salary:- 1st year   nil
     2nd year   £15
     3rd year   £20

Laundry indoor for all, and outdoor for private staff is provided. Nurses may be sent in charge of private cases after two years training and are promoted to posts in the hospital according to their suitability. Three months salary allowed in cases of serious illness.

(Reproduced from the Queen Elizabeth Hospital Nurses League Magazine 1971) qualification of State Registered Nurse. By the 1920's courses for this qualification were operating at the Queen's Hospital but it should be noted that well before then Queen's Hospital Matron, Miss Mary Cadbury, had established a form of in-house training and gave regular lectures to nurses in the mid 1890's.

In developing this book we were able to talk to two nurses who had trained at the Queen's Hospital between the late 1920's and 1930's and some information relating to the rules and regulations of the day were discovered.

The first point to note here was that in the early 1930's new nurses were required to bring the uniform which she (or her parents) had to provide. As can be seen in Figure 4, the list includes some 'essentials' to maintain the room, namely the dusters, pin trays etc. It appears there were strict rules about the display of these goods and as noted, only the pincushion and pin tray could be placed on the dressing table in the nurse's room. Only one text book was recommended – the physiology text by Furneaux

The nurses who trained and worked at the Queen's Hospital remember a very formal and structured routine which reflected the model of nursing of the day. Some differences can be seen between the new probationer (the title given to student nurse in those days) who began her training in October in 1929 and the one who began in 1936. The first of these remembered receiving brief instructions on arrival and being allocated a bed with other new probationers in a basement. She was told to report for duty at 7 o'clock next morning on a male surgical ward; having had no practical nursing classes. Compulsory theoretical instruction was given by Sister Tutor in early years and later on the doctors gave lectures; but all this happened in off duty which was limited to 2 hours daily,

---

Figure 1.3
List of requirements – The Queen's Hospital probationers (1931)

Uniform:
  6 White linen belts
  2 Plain print dresses (as pattern)
  14 Aprons – square bibs and straps.
  8 pairs cuffs
  6 Collars
  1 pair Surgical silver-plated scissors (stamped with name)
  2 Clothes bags (name worked half way down in letters 2 inches deep)
  Black woollen stockings
Other:
  2 Dusters
  1 Pincushion   } these alone graced one's
  1 Pin-tray 8 inches long   } dressing table
  1 Physiology book by Furneaux

with *"an occasional half day and no days off"*.

The Queen's Hospital offered wide clinical experiences. The probationers remembered working on many wards, one especially enjoying surgical experiences. Memories of one nurse who arrived as a new probationer in 1929 (spending 1929 to 1933 in training) were of the wards run in a punctilious manner, but 'the atmosphere was always good'. Both interviewees remember the patients were usually bed-fast for several weeks, with visitors only twice weekly. Despite the hard regime these nurses remember patients regarding their nurses as 'angels' and always being very grateful for their care. This contrasted with their recognition of the assessment by the Lady Almoner who determined the ability of patients to contribute to the cost of their care and treatment – this was not always appreciated !

Ward nurses consisted of Sister, Senior and Junior Staff Nurses, Senior and Junior Probationers. It was necessary for nurses to pass the General Nursing Council Preliminary State Examination (see Chapter 3) to move from Junior to Senior Probationer status. The ward sisters who *'all seemed old'*, and the staff nurses, were responsible for teaching nursing skills, formally or informally. The nurses remembered the Staff Nurses as the great role model for the Probationer, teaching new nursing skills. The nurses also remembered attending lectures by a number of the many honorary (Consultant) doctors almost always in 'off duty time'.

The senior nursing staff also made an impact. The Queen's Hospital Matron during the early 1930s was a Miss Bullivant. She was held in high esteem and remembered for her rounds of the ward, talking to both the patients and probationers, keeping up the atmosphere of courtesy that pervaded the hospital at that time. At the same time Miss E.Collett was the Night Superintendent, remembered for her wards rounds which were 'testing times'. She later moved to the new Centre Hospital.

The off duty patterns were strictly set with little available free time. The working day for probationers, for example, began at 6.30 a.m. with breakfast, working from 7.00 a.m. with short breaks until 8 p.m. The night duty hours were also long – 12 hour shifts with just one day off every month. It was noted that Night Nurses must be in bed by 12 mid-day on week-days and by 1.15 p.m. on Sunday. During night duty nurses lived in a house on Hagley Road to enable rest.

The meagre salaries for the years 1929–1933 provided the probationer with £20 in the last nine months of the first year, having received no remuneration for the very first three months; this rose to £25 in second year and £30 in third year. Having achieved State Registration, it became £40 in the fourth year. Probationers were not required to pay for food, accommodation or laundry. On night duty the junior probationer was required to prepare the meal for the senior

Figure 1.4
The Queen's Hospital, Birmingham: Rules for Nurses 1933

Punctuality must be observed in the performance of all appointed duties, and special attention in this particular is called to the STATED hours for entering and quitting wards, for meals, for lectures, and for classes.

Beds must be aired and the bedroom windows opened. Nurses must sweep and dust their rooms and put them in order and make their beds during the half-hour allowed for dressing.

Nurses must retire to their bedrooms by 10 p.m. and lights must be out by 10.30 p.m.

No Nurse is allowed to visit another Nurse's bedroom after 10 p.m.

Baths are not allowed to be used by the Nurses without special permission after 10.30 p.m.

Nurses suffering from ailments, even if slight, including sore throats, lack of sleep, or septic fingers must at once report them to the Matron.

Night Nurses are expected to go out for an hour daily, and to be in bed by 12 noon.

Nurses when on night duty must not leave their Wards, without permission, except in cases of emergency to call for help.

Nurses when off duty may not enter the Wards or any other working department of the Hospital without permission.

Nurses may be visited by friends when off duty in the afternoon, but on Sundays and Wednesdays after 4 p.m. only.

The Hospital Telephone may not be used by Nurses either for receiving or sending private messages. In case of emergency permission is granted by the Matron.

Nurses may not visit former Hospital patients in their own homes nor accept presents other than flowers from either in or out patients.

Nurses wishing to see the Matron will find her in her office every weekday at 8.45 a.m.

(Source: Supplied by Kathleen Boggon to the Queen Elizabeth Hospital Nurse League Magazine 1991)

Figure 1.5
The Queen's Hospital, Birmingham:
Regulations concerning probationer nurses – 1933

I   Applicants desirous of being trained as Nurses shall produce certificates of age and health and testimonials of character. Age from 19 to 33 years. Probationers will not be engaged without a personal interview. The expenses of interview shall be borne by the candidate. An interview does not guarantee an engagement.

II   Nurses shall be subject to the Laws, Bye-Laws and Rules and Regulations of the Hospital.

III   They shall be required to serve as Assistant Nurses in the Wards, receiving instruction from and being subject to the Ward Sisters. they shall keep the apartment allotted to their use clean, neat, and in proper order.

IV   They shall be required, when on duty in the Hospital, to wear the uniform approved by the Nurse Committee, and to provide the uniform necessary for their first three months.

V   They shall receive board, lodging and washing at the expense of the Hospital. At the expiration of three months, if accepted, Probationers shall receive indoor uniform.

VI   She shall not receive any salary for the three trial months of service unless accepted for training. If during the trial period any candidate contemplates declining to enter into the following Agreement, she shall be required to give a month's notice before leaving.

VII   The Nurse shall be required to pass the Hospital's and enter for the State Examinations, paying her own fees for the latter. Nurses and Probationers are required to serve in any department of the Hospital at the direction and under the control of the Matron acting under the authority of the Nurse Committee. Repeated failure to pass any Hospital or State Examination will render the Nurse's Engagement liable to reconsideration by the Nurse Committee.

VIII   After three months training every Probationer, if accepted, shall enter into an Agreement with the Hospital in the following terms:

1.   The Nurse shall serve the Hospital as Nurse for four years, computed from the .... day of ....

2.   During the whole term of service she shall conform to the Rules and Regulations of the Hospital, and shall discharge such duties as the Matron, acting under the authority of the Nurse Committee shall direct.

3. The Hospital shall, during the Nurse's service, provide her, or cause her to be provided, with board, lodging, uniform and washing.

4. During the first year of service she shall be paid at the rate of £20 per annum

   During the second year of service she shall be paid at the rate of £25 per annum

   During the third year of service she shall be paid at the rate of £30 per annum

   During the fourth year of service she shall be paid at the rate of £40 per annum.

5. In case of any breach of any Law, Bye-Law, Rule or Regulation of the Hospital, or in case of unfitness, misconduct, disobedience, or failure to discharge her duty, a Nurse may be suspended, by the Matron, and may be discharged by the Nurse Committee.

6. This Agreement may be terminated by the Nurse Committee upon the Matron's recommendation.

7. In case of prolonged illness during the period of training, a Nurse may be required to serve such time after expiration of the four year's service as the Nurse Committee may decide.

8. Upon completing her four years' engagement to the satisfaction of the Nurse Committee, and of the Matron, she shall receive a Certificate of Training.

Date: ....   Matron.

N.B. The Matron may be seen on Wednesdays and Fridays at 3.30 p.m. by appointment.

(Source: Supplied by Kathleen Boggon to the Queen Elizabeth Hospital Nurse League Magazine 1991)

probationer and herself, during their 12 hour shift.

The probationer who started training in 1936 also remembered receiving the same £20 in their first year, but, by this time they no longer had to provide their own uniform. Differences were noted in the training programme as this probationer received some 6 weeks instruction in basic practical nursing skills, anatomy, physiology and hygiene classes when they started their programme. The classes were given to the group of nine probationers by Sister Tutor D. Winnett in the hospital basement which served as classroom. During the six introductory weeks this group made short visits to the wards to become accustomed to that environment. Following this these junior probationers were allocated to wards, where initially they did a lot of cleaning and very basic nursing duties. Standards were high but the detail was seen as *'overly important'*.

Living conditions
Probationers were required to live in the hospital residence throughout four years and in those years nurses were guided by a clear framework of rules and regulations (Figures 1.4 and 1.5). All probationers lived in very basic accommodation in the Nurses Home, which was ruled by an apparently rather severe Home Sister. Lights had to be out by 10.30 p.m. and a late pass was only granted in very special circumstances.

Social life
As with the working day, off duty time was also subject to general rules as illustrated in Figure 1.6. With the small remuneration and the limited free time,

---

Figure 1.6
General rules relating to off duty (Queen's Hospital)

Absence from wards for recreation two hours daily.

On Tuesday, Probationers off duty from 2.00 to 9.30 p.m.

On Wednesday, all Senior Probationers are off duty from 2.00 to 9.30 p.m.

On Thursday or Saturday, Sisters or Nurses off duty from 2.00 to 10.00 p.m.

Sisters every other Sunday off duty from 4.00 to 10.30 p.m. Nurses and Probationers off duty on Sundays alternately from 9.00 a.m. to 12.30 p.m. or 2.00 p.m. to 9.30 p.m.

Half an hour allowed for meals.

Ward Sisters and Senior Staff Nurses are off duty once a month from Saturday at 2.00 p.m. to Sunday 10.00 p.m. or 9.30 a.m. on Monday if sleeping out.

Probationers are off duty once a month from 2.00 p.m. to 12.00 mid-day on the following day.

Night Nurses have 12 nights off duty, two at a time in each three months of night duty.

NB The time stated on the passes means time of absence from wards.

Matron.

off duty activities were mostly centred on the hospital, specially enjoying tennis, playing bridge, occasionally having parties amongst themselves. Free theatre tickets were often available. It was possible to save money and buy clothes; only a few were needed as much time was spent in uniform. Just occasionally there was enough money (a half-a-crown, 12 1/2 new pennies, went a long way then) to take the tram to town and have tea in a cafe. All this despite being always tired.

A lot of fun was had within the hospital especially at Christmas. At that time wards competed with each other for the best decorated ward; there was a Christmas Show and once a Christmas Dance was allowed in the Out Patients Hall, but it had to end at 9.30 p.m.!

Having become a State Registered Nurse, the role of the probationer changed to that of Staff Nurse. On the ward the Senior Staff Nurse presented the new junior Staff Nurse with strings which were put on under the cap to mark her new status. The fourth year was spent as a Staff Nurse and at its conclusion Matron gave this new State Registered Queen's Hospital Nurse her Badge and Certificate. One of our interviewees remembered gaining a lot of confidence during this year feeling she developed the ability to cope with any eventuality. Sometime later she was awarded the Gold Medal. This nurse later became a Sister Tutor and then spent many years teaching a long series of student nurses for their first 3 months of training in the Queen Elizabeth Hospital Nurse Training School.

Conclusion

Almost one hundred years after the founding of the Queen's Hospital, the new Centre Hospital, later to become the Queen Elizabeth Hospital, was opened. Both came about as a result of the earnest endeavour of public spirited men and women who contibuted to these developments.

The nurse who trained in 1936 to 1940 had clear memories of the development of the new Centre Hospital which would result in the closure of the Queen's Hospital. At that time the probationers were remote from this, although one of these did attend the opening of the new Centre Hospital in July 1938. Many of the staff of the Queen's Hospital transferred to the new Centre Hospital and took their experience and high standard arising out of this with them. It is for this reason the Queen's Hospital was seen as the precursor to the Queen Elizabeth Hospital.

Chapter 2

The Queen Elizabeth Hospital

The story of caring at the QEH site can be traced back to around AD 50–60 if the location of the hospital is reviewed. The map illustrated shows a Roman Camp, two in fact, one inside the other. As can be seen the present Medical School lies across the north-eastern corner of the map. The camps are dated at about AD 50–60, at a time when the frontier was being pushed forward to Wroxeter in Shropshire and Wall near Lichfield. Hutton in his History of Birmingham refers to "the campus in Metchley Park, Edgbaston". Armed forces encamped in hostile territory would have had some form of medical services, so these would be the earliest doctors and carers of Metchley prior to development of the QEH.

Despite these early origins for the purpose of this book, we may set the opening of the story in 1925. The two teaching hospitals – the Queen's and the General – were faced with an increasing demand for beds which they were unable to meet, and both were considering proposals for extensions involving heavy capital expenditure. By 1925 the authorities realised that there were too few hospital beds for the city's residents. The Voluntary Hospitals Council set up a committee under Sir Gilbert Barling to improve the situation through heavy capital expenditure at the General and Queen's hospitals. This Council had approved the Queen's Hospital scheme, and work had actually begun when a munificent offer of a pleasant site of 150 acres, close to the University of Edgbaston, was received from Messrs. Cadbury Bros. Ltd for hospital purposes. Cadbury Brothers were famed for their chocolate made at the site located in Bournville about a couple of miles from what was to be the Hospital site.

The Hospitals Council thereupon requested the governing bodies of the two hospitals to curtail their schemes for development, and "*to meet and consider the outline of a scheme for a new Hospitals Centre*". The invitation was accepted, and a committee was set up and, in due course, issued a unanimous report (generally known as the Grant Robertson Report, after its chairman), which recommended that a Hospitals Centre should be established at Edgbaston under the joint control of the General and Queen's Hospitals, and that the two hospitals should be amalgamated for all purposes. The University of Birmingham had

THE METCHLEY ROMAN FORTS.

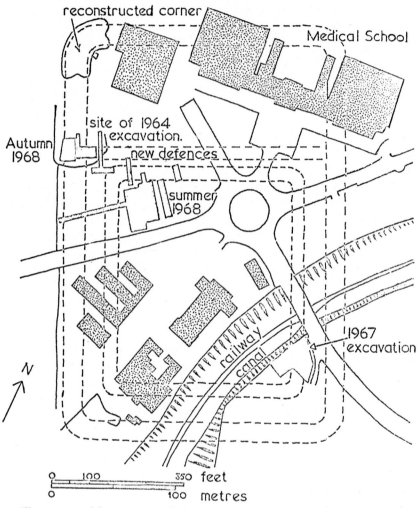

Illustration of first century Roman campsite with more recent buildings superimposed.

long wished to transfer the Medical Faculty from Edmund Street to Edgbaston, and the Centre Scheme, the essence of which was the co-ordination of a group of hospitals with the Medical Faculty of the University, made such a move possible.

The Centre Hospital plan was developed specifically to rectify an estimate made that year that showed Birmingham was short of 600–800 hospital beds. A later report in the Journal of the Incorporated Association of Hospital Officers noted that there was "*surrounding land for the erection of grouped specialist hospitals*" (The Hospital 1938). Within the planning process therefore it was noted that other hospitals were to be built on this site which was to be known as the Hospitals Centre. These hospitals were the Ear, Nose and Throat, Eye, Maternity, Women's and Dental Hospitals.

Once the Hospitals Centre Scheme was accepted, an Executive Board was established in 1927, with Sir Charles Grant Robertson as Chairman. The estimated cost of the scheme was one and a quarter million pounds, but it was decided to prepare plans for a first instalment (designed in such a manner that the full scheme could be completed at a later date) at an expenditure of approximately one million pounds. A joint appeal was made and it was agreed that, apart from donations specially allocated, five-sixths of the funds collected should be devoted to the hospital and the remainder to the University of Birmingham for the erection of a new Medical School. The magnitude of the proposal was fully realised, as well as the immensity of the task of those entrusted with the raising of such a huge sum.

Fund-raising

The public were encouraged to provide donations which were asked for in 'generous quantity'. It was interesting to note that requests were made especially for donations of 7 years length as these were tax-efficient! (The Hospital 1939).

After 3 years preliminary work the fund-raising effort was launched in the Town Hall in 1930, and was well supported by every section of the community. There was a lot of debate about the new development as evidenced in correspondence at that time to the newspaper, the Birmingham Post. The controversy surrounding this in 1931 and 1932 resulted in a lost 2 years in developing the new Centre Hospital.

Among many generous contributions was £7500 from the Austin Car Dealer network to honour the Golden Wedding Anniversary of Lord and Lady Austin. Additional money was raised by public subscription with Mr. Harry Vincent (of Blue Bird Toffees) as treasurer and inspirational protagonist. Some £1,158,458 was given in the form of hundreds of donations and legacies and the building cost £1,029,057.

The building of the Centre Hospital commenced in 1933 but, sadly, even by then, costs had risen so much, that the original plan had to be trimmed and losses included some 180 beds (half the West Wing), Out Patients Department, Casualty Block, Night Nurses Wing, Maids' Quarters and the Chapel. The bed complement thus became about 540.

In October 1934 HRH The Prince of Wales (later Edward V11 and Duke of Windsor) laid the foundation stone of the hospital and cut the first sod at the Medical School site. On 1st January 1935, the voluntary hospitals in Birmingham merged to become the Birmingham United Hospitals, pursuant to an Act of Parliament passed in 1934.

QEH – Concept and design
The philosophy of a Hospitals Centre was fundamental to development from the early days of the conception and planning of the Edgbaston site and is stated in the reports of the Hospital's Council from the 1920's. The site included the University of Birmingham's newly built Medical School and this body exerted much influence and authority.

At a meeting of the Birmingham and Five Counties Architectural Association in early 1935, Mr Lodge of Lanchester and Lodge, the architects for the development gave a paper on the new building now rising in Edgbaston. The philosophy was that:

"modern hospital and medical practice demands there shall be organic and integral connection between the scientist and clinician for the most efficient treatment of the patient and is no less necessary for the training of medical students and nurses".

Mr Lodge said the Centre would be a new development for this country with buildings for all classes of patients, (except psychiatric and infectious conditions) being concentrated on one site, with nursing accommodation and a Medical School integral with the University. This could only be seen in Cornell Medical Centre and the Presbyterian hospitals in New York. From a design point of view it was noted that:

"What the Centre can accomplish has been given precedence over its looks. The buildings are therefore devoid of mere ornamentation, reliance being placed on mass and line to secure simplicity, refinement and the quiet grace which expresses the humanitarian character of a hospital".

The Building
It is interesting to note that prior to the hospital being built the land was farmed

Farm land – the space later occupied by the QEH Medical School. Note the university clock tower in the background.

by Mr A Follows whose name no longer appeared in Kelly's Directory by 1934, though A J Follows, Dairyman was established at Mill Farm by Harborne reservoir in 1937, and was still there in the early 1950's. A member of the QEHNL remembered nursing a Mrs Follows who had commented *"we farmed all this land"*. The farming is evident in the picture illustrating the corn stooks.

The open field site next to the University was well placed, but not ideal. It falls fifty feet from North East to South West and was waterlogged. The foundations vary in depth from 6 feet to 27 feet and carry a load of 2 tons per square foot.

These changes in level had a potential benefit in the design of the hospital in that they enabled the mortuary and kitchens to be at lower levels and not in areas frequented by the public. It also permitted Administration to be at ground level with the X Ray Department placed centrally over it. It was originally intended that Casualty would be on the same level as X Ray, being located where the Annexe accommodation was eventually built in 1946. The situation allowed the majority of wards to have South and West facing aspects.

The construction was steel-framed with buff brick facing, and a limited amount of stone decoration. Floors were hollow tile and reinforced concrete, while the roofs were similar with cork and asphalt topping. The windows were metal framed with a fixed lower pane to avoid draughts. (This was not always

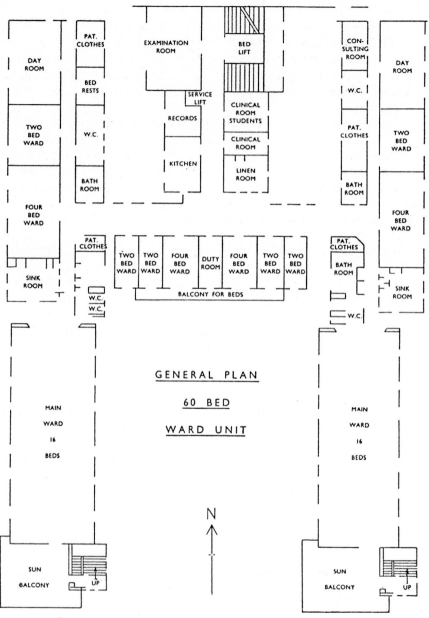

Diagram of the layout of hospital wards in the new QEH.

efficient in function!). The sun balconies were intended to be open-air wards and were used as such for many years (although later enclosed). Ward floors were teak; the corridors were rubber and sanitary room floors (i.e. sluice room, toilets and bathrooms) were terrazzo. As the techniques involved in laying terrazzo floors were very specialised at that time the Italian contractors did this work in seclusion to preserve their trade secrets! Doors were flush, faced in walnut or oak.

The East ward block has two more floors than the West due to the sloping site. The East wards were planned as one unit of 60 beds and labelled as A and B wards to distinguish them. In addition each ward was distinguished by the number of the floor on which they were located thus, for example East 1B indicated the ward was on the first floor of the B side of the East wards. Each ward was made up of two units with 16 beds described as the 'main wards, four units with 4 beds and six units with 2 beds described as 'side wards'. Offices and the kitchen were central to save space (see illustration).

It is not cited specifically, but implied, that a Senior Sister (identifiable by uniform in that she would wear a frilly long cap) would command the floor with a subordinate junior Sister for each side. In later years a legend developed that the sterilising rooms were omitted in the original design and had to be converted as an afterthought. The truth of this mistake in design is confirmed by the illustration in a book outlining the history of the QEH, written by Sir Stanley Barnes, which clearly shows the lack of sterilising room (Barnes 1952)

Ventilation was natural and heating was from five 30 feet by 9 feet diameter boilers in a distant coal fired boiler house supplying heating panels in the ceilings. Water came from a special bore hole, an artesian well, on the site by the boiler house. It is interesting to note that although this was sealed after some years it was reopened much later to supply water to the site. The clock tower of the hospital concealed a large water tank.

The walls in the hospital were painted in enamel paint (gloss). A complex system of coloured lights above doorways in corridors and wards provided a signalling or call system for doctors, while beds had a unit providing a nurse call system, wireless plug and bed light. Much later, probably in the 1950's, piped oxygen was delivered to some beds.

The main operating theatre block of five theatres, each connected to the ward it served by a bridge, was designed on two principles. The first was to keep the theatre "clean" after "it had been scrubbed", by providing a room for the storage of dressings, which are sterilised on the ground floor of the block. The second was to have those things required during surgery at the shortest possible distance from the table. The pillar at the head of the table provided the supply of anaesthetic gases from the ground floor.

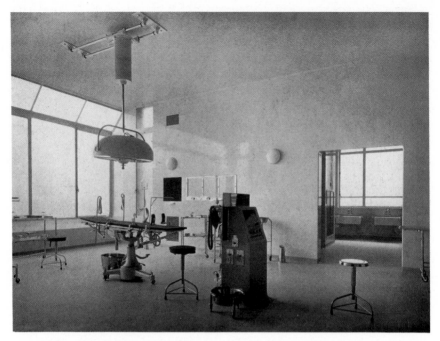

One of five General Operating Theatres, each equipped in the most up-to-date manner and having Surgeons', Nurses' and Students' changing rooms adjoining. There are, in addition, five Specialist Theatres.

The Chapel was built within the Hospital as a temporary arrangement the original plan was that this should be built in the central quadrangle as a discrete building attached to the hospital

It is interesting to note that the original plans included rooms for relatives to stay, a Casualty and an Outpatients Department. The former was to be beyond the West Surgical Block, the latter beyond the East Medical Block. The proposed Casualty was designed with a large central waiting room, four surgery rooms, an operating theatre and twenty beds. The outpatients was to have a hall 102 feet by 41 feet, a canteen, 12 consulting suites and a dispensary at the exit. This original design was to have been amended by abandoning the waiting hall and adopting an appointment system, *"just as in Harley Street"*. However, the second tier of the west wards was never completed in the original design due to shortage of money and the onset of the 1939–1945 war.

It should be noted that for a number of years there were restrictions on site about the type of brick facing that should be used for any additional work to

The Chapel. This room on the first floor was dedicated for Divine Service until it was possible to build the chapel in accordance with the plans for the completed buildings.

keep the concept of the design intact. This however, did not last as is evidenced by more recent development work on site.

Nuffield House (The Nurses Home)
The Nurses Home was occupied in September 1938, a couple of months before the hospital building. The Nurses Home was always known as Nuffield House, named after its generous donor, Lord Nuffield of Morris Motors, at a cost of £500 per bedroom! It was designed to house 300 nurses, rooms for 230 student nurses and 42 sisters, with accommodation for the Matron, Assistant Matrons, and Charge Sisters. This number was based on a formula of the day, which stated that 100 patients required 60 nurses. (Remember the hospital was to have about 540 beds).

Unlike the walls in the hospital which were finished in gloss those in the Nurses' Home were distempered. The 300 bedrooms, were at least 110 square feet each in size. It is thought the room size reflected the required amount of air space for single occupancy given the calculations of environment space of the day, although, the eventual demand on space meant that double

Under the National Health Service Act, 1946, the hospitals which are
together known as the United Birmingham Hospitals are deemed to be a
single hospital. As the teaching hospital of the Midlands, it works in the
closest collaboration with the University of Birmingham in medical training
and research. The above illustration shows the Queen Elizabeth Hospital and
Nuffield House and, on the left, the home of the Medical Faculty of the
University. The splendid site of 150 acres on which the buildings stand
adjoins the University campus at Edgbaston.

bunks were installed and the rooms shared for many years.

Each room had a built-in unit containing a wardrobe, three drawers and two long cupboards, a bureau with three large and two small drawers, with a top that lifted up converting it into a dressing table. By the divan bed with its spring interior mattress was a bedside table and rug. An upright and easy chair were also in the room; a radiator and heated towel rail by the hand basin. Linoleum covered the floor.

Initially it had been intended that a Night Nursing Home should be built to one side of Nuffield House and another for domestic staff the other side but financial constraints had made these an "impossible dream".

The very large reception room on the ground floor was 172 feet long and 44 ft wide. This could be divided by very tall sliding doors into several smaller rooms. This room became commonly known as the 'Rec'. As will be seen in later Chapters this room was the base for many social events ranging from hops, to films to radio shows. The BBC broadcast many orchestral concerts,

A Nurse's Bedroom in Nuffield House each comfortably furnished with a built-in wardrobe and a combined desk and dressing table.

and a TV variety show on Boxing Day 1951, from Nuffield House. Other activities were ongoing in Nuffield house. For example, the Feeney Trust donated a 16mm cine projector for film shows and some nurses remembered a juke box being made available each year for the Christmas holiday time. The Rec. was also used for formal balls which were grand occasions, those attending wore long dresses and gloves and were formally received. In 1948 the surgeon Mr B. N. Brooke organised the first staff Art Show which had a wide variety of exhibits and displayed considerable talents, this continued for some years.

Following the war a large well designed shop was built in the Crush Hall in Nuffield House. Before this supplies were available from a little shop/post room by the front door. Near to the shop were the notice boards on which were displayed Change and Holiday lists (that is the lists allocating nurses to the wards they were due to work on and giving them their holiday entitlement). Further along the corridor was the tunnel which linked the hospital to Nuffield House. The post room was replaced with a reception/post area in the large alcove

Recreation Room, Nuffield House. The Recreation Room, when opened to its
fullest extent, made a splendid ballroom for the Nurses.

Recreation Room, Nuffield House. This magnificent room could be divided by
means of partitions to form two separate rooms at each end, with a large
centred portion as shown in the photograph.

The sixth annual art exhibition of the Medical School and United Birmingham Hospitals was opened at Nuffield House by Professor T. L. Hardy. Our picture shows two student nurses, Miss R. Edwards (left) and Miss A. C. Lovell, inspecting the paintings.
Photograph: Birmingham Post and Mail

at the base of the west staircase; it was manned by receptionist staff who became greatly loved friends to many student nurses.

In 1948 it was noted that a new appointment was to be made, Lady Warden of the Nurses' Home. This was seen as an innovatory appointment as prior to that time all nurses homes were managed by 'home sisters'. This Warden, Miss J. Francis, stayed for 18 months when she left to get married and was succeeded by Miss Lathbury. Miss Francis, *"a lady of distinct personality and social qualities"* organised talks and discussion groups on art and music, and classes in ballet, art and physical culture. Miss May was especially recalled sitting at the reception desk by some of the student nurses who trained in the early 1950's. From this desk, nurses could often get free or discounted tickets for theatres, cinemas and concerts.

A hierarchy existed concerning the seating arrangements in the dining room,

Nuffield House. Nurses making purchases at the shop on lower ground floor.

the more senior nurses sitting nearer the servery and the juniors near the door. For a time the Sisters also ate in this dining room but later moved to their own dining room.

The presence of hierarchy was evident also in the later memories of a nurse who recalled having a 'wake up' knock on the bedroom door at 6 am in the morning and being expected to be in the Dining room for 'roll call' at 6.40 a.m. The dining rooms doors were locked at this time and any nurse not present for roll call was subject to disciplinary action. It appears this system continued until well into the 1950's, as did the night nurses roll call before the night shift.

The opening of the Centre Hospital
The new, vast and imposing Centre Hospital and the Medical School of the University of Birmingham, judged by many to be the finest achievement of modern architecture in Birmingham, constituted the first instalment of the Birmingham Hospitals Centre Scheme.

The hospital and medical school were officially opened by the Duke of Gloucester deputising for King George VI on 14 July 1938 who was ill. The hospital was blessed by the Bishop of Birmingham, who was the brother of Dr.

Stanley Barnes, the then Dean of the Medical School and a great champion of the Hospitals Centre Scheme.

At the end of October 1938 The Birmingham United Hospitals (formed by the amalgamation of the General and Queen's Hospitals) took possession to control and administer the new Centre Hospital as it was 'handed over' by the builders and the hospital was taken over from the contractors on 1st November.

Among the earliest staff appointed to the new Centre Hospital were the Queen's Hospital House Governor, Mr. G. Hurford, to be the new Centre Hospital's House Governor, and the Matron of the General Hospital, Miss G. A. Bowes, to be its Matron. Both were appointed from 1st January 1937. One of their first tasks was to develop a full list of requirements for a 540 bed hospital. This must have been a mammoth task, with no computers, probably few clerks and fewer telephones! It was interesting to note that all the hospital's equipment, linen, stationery, etc. was engraved or marked 'Centre Hospital' .

The Matron (Miss Bowes) and the Principal Tutor (Miss E. Woodhouse) had come from the General Hospital; both were keen to initiate new ideas. Matron Bowes, for example, was intensely proud of the nurses' uniforms which were designed by Norman Hartnell, but incorporated some of her ideas. They were very different from those in other hospitals at that time and for years to come, being in lovely soft colours – corn, blue, mauve and green with brown shoes and stockings, with a short brown and beige cloak. Short caps were worn by student nurses for the first three years of their four year course. The 'long cap' was worn by fourth year student nurses, staff nurses, sisters, and assistant matrons, with variations for each grade (see Chapter 3).

The first student nurses Preliminary Training School (PTS) started in October 1938 and lasted about three months in readiness for the Hospital opening. The student nurses were apparently sent home for a long Christmas holiday, but were recalled after a few days as it was decided to open the hospital and so it came into active service at the end of 1938. One of the people interviewed in this project was a newly appointed staff nurse. She remembered looking back as the doors to the Hospital were locked before Christmas 1938 and asking herself '*I wonder when this hospital will next be completely locked ?*'. To this day it has never been empty and completely locked again.

The first patients were admitted on 31st December 1938 to the first wards to open, East 1A and B, West 1 and West 2. Some qualified staff had, of course, been appointed from the other hospitals in the city and elsewhere and so were experienced nurses. The new Hospital had a very positive impact on the new appointments:

> '*To be a staff nurse trained elsewhere, QE at this time gave favourable impressions – uniform was colourful . . . food was plentiful, excellent*

... served in a pleasant dining room ... informality existed off duty ... early in my training I recall being reprimanded for walking out without hat and gloves! ... a feeling of comradeship existed between all hospital staff... and a deep affection for the hospital developed between patients, relatives, every grade of hospital staff and voluntary workers'.

There were now only eight months ahead of the new Centre Hospital to settle into a routine, before World War II was declared. Immediately that happened on 3rd September 1939, 'blackout' had to be strictly maintained; this was achieved in the wards, by huge thin wooden screens covering the windows; these were erected every evening and taken down every morning by porters.

As will be seen in later Chapters the war played a major role in the development of care in the QEH. With the outbreak of war, the hospital was called upon to accommodate just over double the number of beds for which the existing building was designed, in order to meet civilian and military requirements. The retreat from Dunkirk, the air raids on Birmingham (in which, fortunately, the QEH suffered no damage) and the stirring events in North Africa brought casualties, and it is interesting that the first wounded from the Normandy invasion arrived in the hospital less than four days after 'D-Day'.

Following the war the next major event was the advent of the National Health Service which. In effect the first ten years of administration under the National Health Service was a period of consolidation and of expansion following the immediate post-war years (see Chapter 5).

The early years

It was noted that *"From early July (1938) a great variety of furniture and equipment began to arrive. Its sorting and allocation was a task of great complexity, but order emerged from chaos"*. and by early December, wards were becoming ready for occupation, though lacking smaller essentials. The organisation of the Kitchen Department was started early and the Ladies Linen League (the predecessor to what became known as the League of Friends) gave great support by raising money, buying materials and sewing night-dresses, pyjamas, masks and, in 1 week, providing 150 pillow slips.

The Annual reports of the Board of Governors for the Birmingham United Hospitals, available in the local library, provided a lot of information about the developments of the early years of the new Centre Hospital, later to become the QEH and are a key source of reference for this section. It should be noted that other committees cited below reported to the Board of Governors.

The new Birmingham United Hospital Board held its first meeting in the

Board Room on 13 December 1938. It was interesting to note that in this report the Hospital Board accepted the new 96 hour fortnight would be desirable for nurses, but could not yet be implemented (as can be seen in Chapter 5 it took a number of years before this pattern of working hours was adopted). The reports also noted that:

"increases in nurses' salaries are inappropriate because of the full facilities for specially organised training and teaching of the probationer or student nurse, which in recent years has shown such a marked improvement, that there is no immediate call for increases in the scale of remuneration for nurses in training".

The Board did however,

"recognise the need to improve the salaries of fully trained nurses, and as and when the opportunity arises, it will do its utmost in this direction".

In this same report the Matron, Miss Bowes, gave great praise to the nurses who tackled any task they were given. She named two new Assistant Matrons, Miss Irwin and Miss Mackinnon. There were still many problems but these were being resolved and an adequate efficient nursing service was being provided. There may have been some criticism levelled at the new hospital as she particularly noted the high nurse to patient ratio, for its time, due to the large number of side wards. Similarly, the House Governor had noted that comparisons between a new developing hospital and well established institutions were not helpful. Miss Bowes was very complimentary about the lecture theatre, classrooms and teaching equipment. She also noted that the first 36 nurses, were ready for the wards as required. (It should be noted that there is some discrepancy in the number of nurses said to have started on the hospital wards at this time as some records indicate there were 34 and other refer to 40)

The hospital, recognised as a showpiece of technology and all that was modern and good in medicine of the day, received a multitude of visitors numbering 10,000 by August 1939. Representatives from many organisations, including numerous overseas visitors, were escorted by staff and voluntary guides.

The Official Opening (1939)
The delayed visit of King George VI and Queen Elizabeth happened in March 1939; their visit including not only the Centre Hospital, but also Nuffield House and the new Medical School. In a simple statement *"I name this hospital the Queen Elizabeth Hospital"* Her Majesty Queen Elizabeth (now the Queen

The King & Queen arrive for The Official opening, March 1939.

Mother), bestowed her name upon the great new block of buildings that was now to be known as the Queen Elizabeth Hospital complex. This surprised and delighted those privileged to hear it for this Royal Christening was unexpected by all but a very few. In this happy manner a new chapter was opened in the life of Birmingham and in the history of the continuous fight against disease and suffering. It did however mean that there was a need to re-label all the crockery and cutlery etc. that had previously been stamped 'Centre Hospital' ! Their Majesties toured the hospital and it is rumoured *"the King asked whether the staff were issued with bicycles"!*

One of the interviewees in this project (Miss Thould) remembered being part of the Guard of Honour in the foyer of Nuffield House, as their Majesties entered the Nurses' Home. This Guard then had to race through the tunnels to the Medical School to form another Guard of Honour there.

The year 1939 also heralded a period of great stress with the advent of war and the Governor's Report is almost entirely concerned with this. The Emergency Medical Service (EMS) was put into operation in late August, Professor Cloake and Miss Bowes being appointed as QEH Commandant and Sector Matron respectively putting the hospital on war footing.

Most patients, a total of 572, were evacuated from the 3 hospitals in the group (General, Queen's and the QEH). Large consignments of Government beds were received and made ready. Soon alarm was expressed at the interference with normal work and the hardship caused to the public during the "Phoney War" period. Representations to the Ministry resulted in normal working being resumed. The extra expenditure incurred in the changes to a war time role were met by the Ministry.

The QEH House Committee Report pays tribute to the staff in implementing the measures to put the hospital on a war footing, naming particularly Professor Seymour Barling, Mr R.P. Scott Mason, Matron and House Governor. Given that the hospital was prominently located, very visible from the air and, at that time very light coloured, consideration was given to camouflage. This was deemed impractical, though the ARP (Air Raid Precautions) organised steel shutters for operating theatre windows, Air-raid shelters were located under the grass bank between the present College of Nursing and Nuffield House.

The report for 1940 mentions serious depletion of staff due to war service requirements, and that nurse and other professional training was difficult. Twelve doctors were called up at the outbreak of war, presumably making a big impact on staffing provision. June 1st/2nd saw convoys of wounded arriving from Dunkirk, and later in the year air-raid casualties.

As a result of the war effort the bed complement at QEH in March 1940 was almost double as illustrated in Figure 2.1:

Figure 2.1
Bed Complement March 1940

Normal use: 384

Reserved for emergency: 32

Special Government beds: 620

Total   1036

It was interesting to note a comment in the 1940 Hospital journal that, an average patient stay of 24.3 days 'due to patient profile' suggests criticism from GHB and Queen's as the average patient stay in those hospitals was 16.5 days.

Other changes in service provision were noted. For example, one issue at this time was that the use of radium was banned in Birmingham and 15 beds were found at Wordsley Hospital near Stourbridge. This was rescinded in 1940 and radium treatment returned to Birmingham. It was interesting to note a comment by one of the people interviewed in this project who remembered that any patient being treated with radium needles had to have these removed when the sirens sounded; the needles were put into a lead container which nurses had to take to a safe place deep below the hospital, described as a *"very eerie trip"*.

Proposals to establish a Fracture and Traumatic Hospital at the Queen's Hospital were developing, while the School of Massage there (established in 1929) was moved to QEH where, some years later, it became the School of Physiotherapy. On October 26th the entire Ear Nose and Throat Hospital was evacuated from the city centre in the late hours to the QEH.

On November 22nd-23rd 104 air-raid casualties arrived in the QEH from the city. Tribute was paid in the annual report to all staff and voluntary stretcher bearers. It is thought that the nearest high explosive bomb to QEH was on the derelict farm out-buildings where the School of Physiotherapy is now located.

The resignation of the Matron, Miss Bowes, to marry Mr Whitehurst, manager of the Midland Bank in New Street, was a surprise to most people. At her request her Testimonial Fund was to provide annually a Gold and Silver Medal for the two leading final year nurses. The new Matron, Miss Smaldon took up her duties in August 1940 *"with energy and enthusiasm"*. The House Committee report testified to "true spirit of service shown by all staff".

The 1941 report was very thin, probably due to paper shortage, which persisted for many more years. Comments here relate to other hospitals. The Queen's Hospital, having opened in 1841, was designated Birmingham Accident Hospital on 31st March, just one hundred years later. It was also interesting to note that, Miss Bullivant, the Queen's Hospital Matron, retired; she had qualified there in 1906 she had seen 34 years of service in the Queen's Hospital. It is also worth noting that the Maternity Hospital in Loveday Street, had been offered the opportunity to relocate to the Queen's Hospital prior to its pending closure was but declined as they wished to rebuild on the Edgbaston site. Sadly it took 30 years for this development to materialise..

In the 1942 report the House Committee Report gives a daily bed occupancy of 592.7, the highest number being 675. As there was no hope of the proposed 100 bed pay-block being built, the hospital's own maintenance staff made Ward East 3 suitable for 60 pay beds.

In 1942, the national pay scales were adopted, although this *"involved considerable expenditure"* but the government contributed 50% of the cost (Figure 2.2). Inevitably where nurses' pay was concerned the expected comments were made:

> *"It may well be held that monetary reward alone will not attract the best type of nurse". "Too much importance cannot be given to the status and tone of the training school, the conditions of training, and its scope and efficiency".*

```
                    Figure 2.2
            Annual QEH Pay Scales 1941–42

PAY SCALES      Before April 1941  From April 1941  New 1942
Student 1st year  £18 pa             £30              £40
         2nd year £22 pa             £35              £45
         3rd year £30 pa             £40              £50
         4th year £40 pa             £50              £60
Staff Nurse       £70–80 pa          £90–100          £100–140
Ward Sister       £80–120 pa         £100–150         £130–180
```

In 1943 it was noted there were "no air-raids this year" though there were difficulties of supply of goods and provisions required to keep the service going. Following the publication of the Beveridge Report in 1942, the National Health Scheme is mentioned for the first time and a Post-War Planning Committee set up, but without a nurse-member, though the report commented on 'a heavy burden on the nursing staff'.

The occupancy rate for the hospital over the early years illustrated in Figure 2.3. It is interesting to consider in this that the hospital was designed for 540 in-patients with an average length of stay of 24.3 days as noted above. The massive rise in the peak wars years can clearly be seen.

The report of 1944 illustrated another busy year as it was the year of the Normandy invasion, where at least one QEH nurse (Jenni Starr-Martin, 3rd PTS) served for a while. The hospital was put on standby in early June and the first convoy of 176 casualties arrived on June 9th. A system had been drawn up involving preliminary examination by a Medical Officer to prioritise care needs (referred to as triage) and transport to the wards where casualties were given a hot meal. This worked so well that few changes were made and between 9 June 1944 and 21 March 1945, 53 convoys with 4,004 casualties were received. The

```
              Figure 2.3
      QEH Bed occupancy 1939–1943

        1939     3,165
        1940     5,531
        1941     9,451
        1942    11,989
        1943    12,136
        Total   42,272
```

Committee gratefully thanked doctors, sisters, nurses, domestic staff, porters, Civil Defence and voluntary stretcher-bearers. *"Only by serious overcrowding has the civilian and military service survived".*

The Post War Planning Committee felt the decision to build the Hospital Centre (QEH) to be fully justified and recommended the completion of the QEH site to be an ideal that should be achieved. They also recommended a separation of functions between QEH and the General Hospital Birmingham (GHB).

Once more the perennial problem of residential overcrowding was a major problem and the Finance Committee sanctioned expenditure to build 100 semi-permanent bedrooms for nursing staff. This was deemed *"inconvenient and expensive, but necessary"*. At that time a number of rooms attached to the hospital were known as the "hutments"; it was noted that if these were not needed for accommodation then consideration should be given to the purchase of large Edgbaston houses for hostels.

The report for 1945 welcomed back the twelve members of staff who had gone to the war. This included Brigadiers E. Bulmer, R.K. Debenham, J.M. Smellie F.A.R. Stammers; Lt Cols Clarke, B.C. Tate & A.J. Moffet and Major F. Selby-Tait. No nurses were welcomed back although, as can be seen in Chapter 5, nurses did remember Sisters who had army experience. It is thought they may have returned later or joined QEH in the post war period. One example was Sister Farr who returned to QEH in 1948.

By 1945 most of the wards had reverted to normal size, although a few military patients remained. The bed complements were adjusted to pre war numbers and the day rooms, examination rooms and Massage (later called Physiotherapy) Department resumed their normal roles. There were grave shortages of material including food and fuel for heating, and manpower in all disciplines. These created 'anxious problems' and to cap it all concern was expressed that the hospital was spending £1,000 per day!

The problems with residential accommodation was slightly eased when Barrow Cadbury and his family donated 40 Edgbaston Park Road known as Southfield to be a residence and Preliminary Training School (PTS) for nurses. In addition a licence (for building materials and manpower) had been issued by the Government to build 57 bedrooms near the dispensary.

By 1946 the report noted that four Professors were appointed, namely Professor W. Melville Arnott, Professor F.A.R. Stammers, Professor James Smellie and Professor Hilda Lloyd. Another big change was the death of Mr Mendel Mindelsohn, the chairman of the first QEH House Committee, and the succession of Mr Hamilton Baynes to the post. Mr Mindelsohn was commemorated by a Nurse's Prize named for him.

The authorities had started to come to terms with the changes necessitated

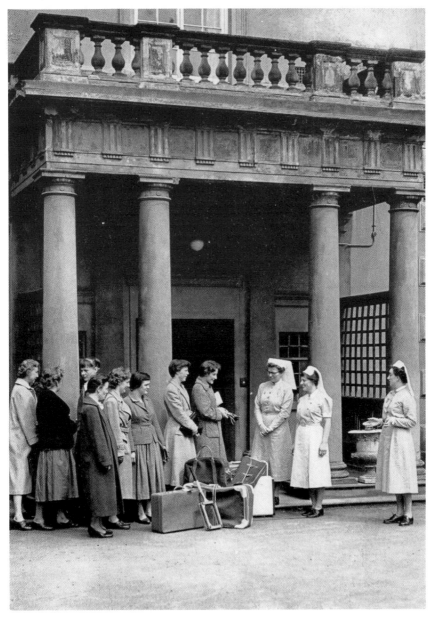

New student nurses arriving at the Preliminary Training School – Southfield, 40 Edgbaston Park Road.

Gardens of the Preliminary Training School – Southfield, 40 Edgbaston Park Road.

by the advent of the NHS. It was affirmed that, the Women's, Maternity, Dental, Eye and ENT hospitals should be erected on the Centre Site as soon as possible. However, priority was to be given to completion of the West Wing, Teaching Annexe, Night Nurses' and Domestic staff residences.

The last report of the Board of Governors of the Voluntary Hospitals was made in 1947. Here it was noted that the Minister of Health had ordered that all major developments were held in abeyance pending the advent of the NHS. This year however saw the establishment of the Clinical Photography Services at QEH.

The beds numbered 587 and would remain so until a Cancer Unit of 63 beds was opened in the North block. A ward kitchen had been fitted with a hot-cupboard which was so successful they were to be installed on all wards. The reduction in patient stay from 21.3 days (1946) to 20.7 (1947) was mentioned, again possibly because of criticism for the same reasons noted above.

The 57 bedrooms that were initially described as the 'hutments' but later became known as the Nurses' Annexe had been completed, but it was reported (with sadness) that over 200 nurses were still in double bunks in single bedrooms in Nuffield House and so approval was given for a further 57 rooms to be built.

In 1948, Miss Richards, hitherto Housekeeping Assistant Matron, was appointed Dietician and Catering Officer. The hospital was now beginning to experience peacetime conditions. The final words in the in 1948 report were:
"We look forward with confidence to the future, when the QEH will stand side by side with her sister teaching hospitals, rendering their unique service to the country".

Advent of the NHS
Sixteen days before the 'appointed day' for the inauguration of the National Health Service, that is on 18th June 1948 the first meeting of the new Board of Governors of the United Birmingham Hospitals (UBH) was held. Prior to that date the group of voluntary hospitals had been known as the Birmingham United Hospital. The Board gave urgent consideration to setting up the new Domiciliary Consultant Service required under the Act. This became operative at 00.01 hours on 5th July 1948, the first call coming in at 00.58 hours and the calling GP was notified that a Consultant Physician was on his way at 01.03 hours.

A new Nursing Advisory Committee was set up comprising five Board Members, five Consultants and the five Principal Matrons of the UBH, the first indication of nurses sitting at a committee table in the UBH having co-equal status with others. This Committee, after preliminary enquiries, adopted a "schedule of reasonable standards" for both working and living conditions for nurses. These detailed minimum conditions for facilities and equipment on wards, and for living accommodation and recreational facilities, which included a music-room. These were accepted in 1949. Wireless reception on two stations had been made available to each bed on the wards, and a TV set bought by the Ladies Linen League for the Radiotherapy Patients Waiting Area and a long-stay TB ward, probably East IB. A shelter with seats was built on the hill from the bus stop and two hard tennis courts provided beyond the small gardens cultivated by Assistant Matrons and Tutors on the west side of Nuffield House.

For the first time in these reports retirements and registrations of senior staff, other than Honoraries (the Consultants) Matrons and House Governors were recorded. Miss McKinnon, Chief Assistant Matron after 12 years service; Miss E. Thould, as Assistant Matron to Torbay as Matron; Miss Ker-Ramsey appointed Deputy Matron 1st September 1950. It was also noted that Mr. A. Tudor, the carpenter, retired in July 1952, having started at the Queen's Hospital in July 1900 and was never late for work in all his 52 years service.

The 1950's
The third Report of the Board covered the years 1952–54. Here it was noted that 'Central' Preliminary Training School opened and a Principal Tutor appointed

to the new Queen Elizabeth School of Nursing (QESN), presumably Miss Whiter. The Matron at this time, Miss Smaldon, went on a study tour of the USA.

In the fourth Report of the Board, April 1954 – March 1956, there is an item of political magnitude in nursing when it was reported that Miss C. A. Smaldon had been appointed Chief Nursing Officer and Principal of the QESN in 1955. It was recognised as a departure from nursing tradition *"but the needs of the UBH and QESN made it necessary and justified"*. Her duties were:

— to advise the Board and Committees on all nursing matters in consultation with the Matrons of the constituent hospitals and to co-ordinate the nursing services within the UBH;

— to act as Principal of the Queen Elizabeth School of Nursing, to whom all tutors are responsible;

— to undertake research in nursing organisation and procedures.

It was stated that while much remained to be done, the integration of training and a steady flow of nurses to the constituent hospitals was in sight. On Miss Smaldon's move to her new role, Miss B. B. Scott, of the Middlesex Hospital was appointed Matron in November 1955.

April 1956 – March 1960 was the period covered by the 5th Report and marks the end of the time span cover in this book. It was interesting to see here that, due to problems of infections originating in the hospital, sterile syringes and needles were to be supplied commercially. At this time also Wards East 3A and East 3B were reconstructed to improve private patient accommodation. Other notable events included the filming of the BBC series, Your Life in Their Hands, which showed a film of Mitral Valvotomy made at QEH. Miss Ker-Ramsey resigned as Deputy Matron in August 1956 to be Matron at George Elliot Hospital, Nuneaton.

Extension plans for a Central Training School were being developed and new classrooms were provided for the Preliminary Training School. A post registration theatre course started. Plans for State Enrolled Assistant Nurses (SEAN, later to be known as State Enrolled Nurses, SEN) training was approved eventually under the aegis of this new school (about 1960). By this time the Central QESN had 1000 students, and Clinical Teachers, a new initiative in education roles for nurses, were being appointed. Third year students were permitted to live out with parental approval and those who married during training were to be greatly encouraged to complete the course. The nurses health was no longer to be in the hands of hospital medical staff. Dr Bence, a local GP, held a regular surgery in Nuffield House for the nurses.

Conclusion

As can be seen above the QEH was a thoroughly modern hospital both in concept and design when it opened in 1938. The plan was to cater for Birmingham's health needs into the twenty-first century but, whilst the caring continued the plan of providing a comprehensive hospital service on site, was foiled by finance, war and politics and the very rapid development of the technology in health care that could hardly have been predicted in the 1930's.

It is interesting to note that the original plan was followed by a similar plan in 1964 to *"develop a comprehensive Hospital Centre for Birmingham'*. In January 1970 approval in principle was given for £8 million to be spent on such a scheme to be completed in 1975, a vision that again, was not fully achieved.

The staff working at the QEH hospital site in the 1990's will have very different memories from their predecessors. They will no doubt relate very strongly to the one flaw in the grand design of the QEH, the dimensions of the proposed car park was minuscule! However, when looking at the spacious drive, uncluttered by cars, on the back cover of this book it is not surprising that transport was not a major consideration.

Chapter 3

The Queen Elizabeth Hospital Nurse Training School

It has been said that a hospital cannot escape from caring for the sick, but it chooses to educate its nurses. The alumni of the Queen Elizabeth Hospital Nurse Training School (QEHNTS) believe that they were well educated and that the instruction they experienced was 'special'. To illustrate this, the chapter will outline the origins of the QEHNTS, elaborate on issues related to the organisation of nurse education and the specific characteristics of this centre that contributed to the 'unique' training experience of the student nurse.

It was interesting to note at the outset that Miss Woodhouse, the first Principal Tutor, was horrified to discover that the original plans for the development of the QEH had not included a practical classroom in which to teach nursing skills. One had to be hastily converted from a Trunk Room in Nuffield House where luggage was stored. However, Miss Woodhouse was delighted that the Centre Hospital had no brass for her student nurses to clean and polish!

As with other issues relating to the hospital, information concerning nurse training was drawn from the Reports of the Boards of Governors available in the local libraries.

The training school at QEH began with the first group, commonly referred to by the number allocated to their Preliminary Training School (PTS), on October 4th. 1938 (about three months before the hospital opened to patients.) and lasted until the 68th. PTS who commenced on July 16th. 1957 completing 4 years later in 1961. In those 23 years over 1700 qualified as a registered nurse as indicated in Figure 3.1. The details of all intakes in the time span covered by this text, can be found in the Appendix. It should be noted that the first male nurse is recorded as entering the programme with the 25 PTS.

Of the first Group in 1938 the Matron's (Miss Bowes) report noted she was pleased to say that 36 student nurses emerged from the Preliminary Training School in time for the hospital to open (although as noted in Chapter 2 this may have only been 34). It was interesting to note the use of the title 'student nurse'. this was quite innovatory at the time as, up until that point nurses in training were referred to as 'probationers'.

Figure 3.1
Total number of student nurses – QEH Nurse Training School
(1938–1957)

Total Number Student Nurses entered = 2456
No. females = 2427
No. males   = 29

Total Number Student Nurses Qualifying = 1759
No females = 1746
No males   = 12

Percentage Achieving SRN   = 71.6%
Successful females = 71.9%
Successful males   = 45%

The next intake of 20 was enrolled for January 1939 and the rate of applications was high so it was felt that selection might prove a problem. Already Miss Bowes was forecasting problems with bedroom accommodation for nurses and domestic staff. Nevertheless she felt that

"*improved working conditions, satisfactory living accommodation and healthy surroundings reflected in a good staff health record*".

It was noted that attention should now be given to the provision of a library and social occasions, due to the comparative isolation of the hospital.

Examination systems
From this early start the QEHNTS went from strength to strength. It was, in common with all training schools at the time, working under the guidelines required by the General Nursing Council for England and Wales (GNC) which was the statutory organisation accountable to Government for the preparation and subsequent registration of nurses at State level. It alone could award the qualification of State Registered Nurse (SRN), the goal to which all the new student nurses arriving at the QEH aspired.

The examination system was rigidly prescribed by the GNC. The Preliminary State Examination (commonly referred to by the students as the 'prelims') were taken at 12 to 18 months. It was possible for some students to have completed part of this on other courses before starting general training. Success was required to be able to continue training. The Final State Examinations were taken at the end of the third year and success in these led to the award of the qualification – State Registered Nurse (SRN). The examinations consisted of written, oral and practical components and, where possible, these were taken on site in the training school. However, sometimes it was necessary for student nurse to travel to other hospital sites to complete these exams as the GNC designated some areas as examination centres at different times. Success in the GNC examinations entitled the nurse to be awarded a GNC badge and Registration Number which was the public evidence that she was fully registered. As will be seen later (in Figure 3.2) students were expected to pay a fee for entry to the GNC examinations.

It should be noted that despite this 3 year pattern of examinations set by the GNC the QEHNTS expected the student nurses to complete a four year training programme. Examinations were taken at the end of the PTS and, if unsuccessful, students were not allowed to continue on the course. A final hospital examination was taken prior to the State examination and student nurse who were unsuccessful in this were not allowed to take the Final State Examination. The four year training period enabled the nurse to work as a junior staff nurse and consolidate her training as a registered nurse. This was quite usual in teaching hospitals that had emerged out of the old voluntary system and was a continuation of the model that had been adopted at the Queen's Hospital (see Chapter 1). It was only on successful completion of four years training that the nurse was entitled to be awarded a QEHNTS badge and the QEH Certificate.

The Queen Elizabeth Hospital Nurse Training School Badge
The hospital badge was the means by which nurses were able to distinguish their training school and is quite an important feature of the nurses uniform and worn with some pride. The badge was brown in colour reflecting the brown shoes and cloak, of the QEH uniform. It consisted of a bar and octagonal badge, and was worn centrally at the neck linking the two parts of the white soft uniform collar together.

The design of the QEHNTS badge depicts a cockatrice taken from the crest of the General Hospital which in its turn is founded on the crest of Dr Ash (the founder of the GHB). The field of the shield indented of gold and blue, is derived from the arms of the ancient family of Edgbaston. The ermine field of the chief, the red bows in the left paws of the lion are derived from the arms of Bowes and the lions from the arms of the Lyon (paternal arms of Queen Elizabeth the Queen mother) and commemorate the naming of the Queen Elizabeth Hospital by Her Majesty the Queen Mother. The dolphin is the chief taken from the arms of the Tippetts in commemoration of the gift by Miss D. E. Tippett of the fee for the grant of the arms. The badge was granted in 29 April 1939.

THE BIRMINGHAM UNITED HOSPITAL
THE GENERAL HOSPITAL, THE QUEEN ELIZABETH HOSPITAL
(INCORPORATING THE QUEEN'S HOSPITAL 1841–1941)

THE QUEEN ELIZABETH HOSPITAL

NURSES' CERTIFICATE
This is to certify that
Doreen Mary Tennant

entered the Training School of the Queen Elizabeth Hospital on the fifth day of September, 1944, has completed a course of four years instruction in the theory and practice of Nursing and has duly satisfied the Examiners that she has acquired a thorough knowledge of her profession.

E P Krecurdu
Chairman of the
Board of Management

M H maldon.
Matron

B. T. Ross
Chairman of the
Medical Committee

G. Kirby
House Governor

Dated this   fourth   day of September 1948

QEH Nurses' certificate.

Miss C. A. Smaldon (Matron) presenting QEH nurses certificates to two new 'long cap blues'. Circa 1944.

The uniform

The uniform of the QE hospital was, as indicated in Chapter 2, unique. Each nurse was measured for her uniform, which, until 1942, they had to purchase themselves. The dresses cost 13/ 4d each. The twelve aprons cost 3/- each and the four caps were 1/7d each and the cape was 16/8d. This totalled £5 12s 4d paid by the student nurses and six pairs of mercerised lisle fawn stockings had to be obtained. In addition they had to purchase uniform brown shoes which cost 21/- (1–05 pounds) in 1940 and £5 in 1952.

For the first two years corn yellow dresses with soft white collars and cuffs were worn. For the last two years of training corn flower blue dresses, again with soft white collars and cuffs were worn. On the wards large aprons were worn. These were the same length as the dresses and covered the whole skirt, secured at the waist by two detachable shanked buttons and at the neck onto two more buttons. The emphasis in the well designed uniforms was the unusual colours, yellow, blue, then mauve, complete without aprons. With these went beige stockings and brown shoes and a two coloured brown cape (most hospitals retained black shoes and stockings for many years to come).

Unusually for the day the QEH had no outdoor uniform but all nurses had

QEHNTS Badge. Photograph by Gary Brown.

strict instructions that they were not permitted to wear their uniform dresses under coats. One of the first purchases commonly made by student nurses was the special Queen Elizabeth Hospital scarf and this was proudly worn when off duty, as it was recognised and honoured by some retailers who gave discounts. These helped eke out the low salaries (training allowances) which amounted to less then £9–12 pounds monthly.

This uniform, illustrated on the front cover and in pictures throughout this book, was quite important in demonstrating progress though the training programme as the yellow dress indicated junior students and the blue dress indicated the senior student nurse status. The short cap, worn in such a way as to cover the maximum amount of hair, also indicated status. The short caps, a triangular piece of very starched printed organdie, was formed with the help of gold safety pins and fixed by white hair grips to cover half the hair.

In the 1950's student nurses who had passed their Preliminary State Examinations were given white caps with a lace trim. At this time also, blue epaulettes were introduced to indicate students were in their second year.

Success in State Final Examination resulted in being awarded a long cap to mark the new status. This was a near square of starched organdie which was folded into three, held by gold safety pins, and fixed to the hair with white hair grips or even a hat pin! The senior staff nurses cap was similar although the fabric was prettier. The long cap was also worn by Sisters (who wore green dresses of a similar design) although the Assistant Matrons and some other senior sisters wore a rather more frilly design. The Queen Elizabeth Hospital caps were well liked, especially the long ones received after gaining State Registration.

From about 1942 students no longer had to pay for their uniform. Female student nurses were issued with four dresses and twelve aprons specifically made to measure for each nurse with the lower hems being 15 inches from the floor. This allowance enabled the students to send two dresses and six aprons to the hospital laundry each week.

Male nurse, when they joined the QEHNTS (see Chapter 6) wore white tunics and trousers and their level of training was indicated by wearing yellow, blue, mauve epaulettes.

The Training System

As noted in the previous Chapter, Miss Bowes was succeeded by Miss Smaldon who was seen to be one of the great innovators of the day in terms of nurse education. She took a lead role in promoting new shift systems of working, introducing lectures from staff at the medical school, supporting the men who wanted to be nurses and changing the system of education as noted below.

The Block Training system (1943)

In 1943 the Matron of QEH , Miss Smaldon persuaded the Committee to introduce the 'Block System' of training for student nurses. She discussed this in a Nursing Times article in 1944, P808. Its features were:

> 12 weeks Preliminary Training School; 6 week's study each year with 1 week's revisions block to both the Preliminary examination and State Finals. Post-registration nurses did 1 week's introduction then followed the pattern from the 2nd year.

Miss Smaldon decided 12 months later that if only around 6 months were spent on the ward in the first year, there would be too little emphasis on nursing practice and the first year block was abandoned, but re-introduced later as a shorter block of three weeks. Nevertheless, although war pressures made withdrawal of nurses from the wards difficult she felt the advantages outweighed the disadvantages for all concerned.

In 1944 the QEHNTS took part in a major innovation, the development of the film, called significantly, "Student Nurse". This was to be used in the UK and abroad to support the recruitment to nursing, at that time beginning to suffer. The commentary was mainly compiled by Miss Smaldon. This was translated into 20 languages and shown in cinemas around the country and around the world. One of the interviewees in this project noted:-

"It caused quite a stir amongst us. Several of the scenes were filmed in the wards and I well remember assisting Sister Westbrook to do a dressing on Ward W3 in front of the cameras. It took nearly all morning to film and took only about two minutes of screen time!

Another remembered one of her PTS group acting as a "star". One of the other six nurses used in the film was Mrs Elinor Hart, nee Griffiths-Jones of the 15th.PTS.

Sometime during 1945–46 a lovely house 'Southfield' in Edgbaston Park Road belonging to the Cadbury family was given to QEH. This gift continued their wonderful generosity, the hospital being built of course on Cadbury donated land. This house was to be the home and school for the intakes of student nurses during the important first weeks of training. The first group, (24th PTS) arrived in April 1946 found it a happy place; the huge lounge was the classroom and the old coach house the practical room; bedrooms were large sleeping 3–6 new nurses. A Home Sister looked after their welfare and the house; nurses took it in turns to sit by her at meal times. The house had huge gardens and a much used tennis court. Most relished their time at Southfield, enjoying independence but there were moments of homesickness too. The school rooms in Southfield were initially within the house, but later a purpose built school wing was added.

By 1946 recruitment to nurse training was reported as adequate, though Matron reported increased wastage among students and qualified staff. She pointed out that to increase student numbers without adequate trained staff would increase the burden on Ward Sisters.

It was noted that student nurses were to go to the Children's Hospital for the first time to gain paediatric experience as required by the General Nursing Council.

The new shift system devised by Miss Smaldon and designed to stop the split working days nurses did up to that point, was piloted on a medical and surgical ward in 1946.

In 1947 there was still a high wastage rate of student nurses though recruitment was sufficient but many applicants were thought unsuitable. The Committee expressed its indebtedness to Matron for the modern innovations she had instituted. These included the Block System of Education, a modern Shift System and an 8 hour day (6 days a week) introduced this year, although there was difficulty in reconciling the claims of service and education.

It was noted in the report of 1948 that the various schools of nursing in the group of hospitals comprising the Birmingham United Hospitals started the slow moves to evolving as a Central School of Nursing, which by order of King George V1 was to be called the Queen Elizabeth School of Nursing (QESN). The word "hospital" was deliberately omitted to avoid one hospital being seen as dominant when student nurses would be training in a number of different hospital sites including, for example the General Hospital Birmingham.

Another innovation during 1948–50 was the Professional Nurse Training Committee. It was chaired by the Dean of the Medical Faculty, Sir Leonard Parsons and its Chief Executive Officer was Miss Smaldon. The membership comprised the Principal Tutor; the matrons of the constituent hospitals; the Professors of Paediatrics and Obstetrics and Gynaecology and Social Medicine; Chairman of Nurse Advisory Committee ex officio; 9 representative ward/ departmental sisters from the five hospitals. The Committee was to explore the new syllabus of training for nurses, also that for assistant nurses (see Chapter 2), of whom this is the first mention. It was to take responsibility for the new school of nursing and recommend methods of training, both Statutory and experimental.

The second Report of the Board covered the period 1950–52, when great strides were made in the Board's policy for nursing services and particularly in the establishment and growth of QESN. A new general training scheme was approved with paediatric and gynaecology experience being gained in specialist hospitals, and a 4 year combined course started for a dual qualification as a State Registered and a Registered Sick Children's Nurse (RSCN).

As plans for the Central Preliminary Training School of QESN were developing it was necessary to look for more space to house the students. This problem was reconciled by leasing a large house known as Priorsfield, which was next door to Southfield, already used as a PTS school for the QEHNTS. Despite the concept of the Central Training School it should be noted that, initially, student nurses from the QEH who lived in Southfield never met students from the General Hospital Birmingham who lived in Priorsfield.

In the fourth Report of the Board, April 1954 – March 1956, there is an item of nursing which noted there had been building developments at the PTS; and joint training schemes with local psychiatric hospitals approved. Approval for the training of State Enrolled Assistant Nurses (SEAN) had been rejected as, at that time, the GNC did not support schools of nursing offering courses for both enrolment and registration. It was at this time that Miss Smaldon's new role, outlined at the end of Chapter 2, was introduced.

Student Committee
At some point in the early 1950's a Student Committee was established. Here student nurses met with the Principal Tutor, the Assistant Matron and the House Governor at three monthly intervals to discuss areas of concern. This was seen as a means of enabling students to make representation about the conditions in which they worked. One success noted as a result of this committee was the building of a shower in the male nurses' changing room in Nuffield House. This was as a result of the male nurses noting they did not have comparable facilities to the residential female student who could bathe at the end of duty.

The training experience
In the course of this project we asked people who had trained at the QEHNTS to recount their memories. A number are absorbed into general nursing issues in subsequent chapters but some are recounted here. The experience was guided by the conditions of service illustrated in Figure 3.2 below. The Conditions of Service illustrated are the Pre-NHS ones (i.e. before 5th July 1948) but corrections have been made, which indicate that they were sent out to prospective student nurses after the NHS. However, the title "Birmingham United Hospital" was not altered to the post-NHS one of "United Birmingham Hospital". It is also interesting to note some other discrepancies in the text in that, for example, reference was made to student nurses working split shifts yet this had been abandoned in favour of the fixed rota of shifts. The reasons for such discrepancy are not know but it is surmised that it may be due to shortage of paper at the time resulting in a wish to use existing stock. It should also be noted that from the male nurse perspective the same conditions of service were issued but each time 'she' or 'her' occurred it was changed to 'he' or 'his'.

It is interesting to compare these conditions of service and salary levels with those of the nurse at the Queen's Hospital in Chapter 1.

Figure 3.2
Queen Elizabeth Hospital Conditions of Service for Student Nurses

QUEEN ELIZABETH HOSPITAL

CONDITIONS OF SERVICE FOR STUDENT NURSES WHO ARE
CANDIDATES FOR ADMISSION TO THE GENERAL PART OF THE STATE
REGISTER OF NURSES

CONDITIONS OF ACCEPTANCE

1.   Every candidate is asked to complete and return the Application Form
      to the Matron and is required to attend the Hospital for a personal
      interview at her own expense.
2.   Candidates should be between the ages of 18 and 33.
3.   Before being accepted every candidate is required to furnish evidence
      of a good general education, references as to character, an official
      copy of her birth certificate and satisfy the Matron as to her health by
      certificates on the prescribed forms.
4.   Candidates are also required to undergo a medical examination at the
      Hospital by a member of the Hospital Staff.

PRELIMINARY TRAINING SCHOOL

5.   Candidates will be required to enter the Preliminary Training School
      for a 6 weeks' course of instruction. During such training candidates
      will be paid at the rate of £40 per annum and will be provided with
      board, lodging and laundry, as well as with the official indoor uniform
      prescribed by the regulations in force. [1] The uniform issued is the
      property of the Hospital and no part of it may be retained by the nurse
      when she leaves the services of the Hospital.[2] Candidates are
      expected to supply themselves with regulation shoes and stockings
      for duty.

TRIAL PERIOD

6.   On completion of the 6 weeks' Preliminary Training School course,
      approved candidates will be admitted to the Hospital as student
      nurses for a trial period of 12 weeks. During this period their services
      may be terminated if they are found unsuitable in any respect, or the
      candidate, if she finds practical hospital work uncongenial, may leave
      at her own request upon giving notice to the Matron.

CONDITIONS OF ENGAGEMENT

7.   Student nurses are accepted for training by the Nursing Committee
      upon the recommendation of the Matron, and subject to a satisfactory
      health report, and must have successfully completed a trial period of
      18 weeks' in all (6 weeks at the Preliminary Training School and 12
      weeks' trial in the Hospital). They are then required to sign an
      agreement by which they are received as student nurses in training
      for the State Registration Examinations. The agreement will cover a
      period of four years training, in which the preceding 18 weeks will be
      included.

---

[1]   Coupons will be surrendered in accordance with the requirements of the
      Board of Trade.
[2]   Shoes 7 coupons, stockings 3 coupons per pair.

THREE YEARS' COURSE
8.   Candidates whose names are entered on one of the Supplementary Registers of the General Nursing Council and candidates who have passed the Preliminary State Examination are accepted for a term of three years' training. Such candidates are not required to pass through the Preliminary Training School and after the trial period rank as second year student nurses. Such candidates are required to undertake the full theoretical course and are subject to the same conditions of service as the four-year students. Salary is payable at the following rates per annum: First Year £65; Second year £75; Third Year £95 after State Registration.

HOSPITAL TRAINING AND EXAMINATIONS
9.   Student nurses are given theoretical and practical training in accordance with the syllabus laid down by the General Nursing Council for England and Wales in the Wards and Special Departments under the Birmingham United Hospital, being instructed by the Sister Tutor and Sisters, and by the Medical and Surgical Staff appointed by the Hospital for the purpose.
10.   Every student nurse will have been prepared for and will be required to have entered for the Preliminary State Examination, Parts I and II, by the end of her first year of training, or at the examination next following. In the event of a student nurse failing to pass the Preliminary State Examination at the second attempt the Nursing Committee may terminate her engagement.
11.   After passing the Preliminary State Examination every student nurse is required to take the Final State Examination, the Hospital undertaking to provide the necessary facilities for her preparation within a period of four years, and also to take the internal examinations, conducted at the Hospital by its own examiners.
12.   Every student nurse who completes her full period of training to the satisfaction of the Nursing Committee, has passed the State Examination[3] and has passed the internal examinations, if any, will be awarded a certificate signed by the Chairman of the Hospital,. The Chairman of the Medical Committee, the Matron and the House Governor of the Unit.

CONDITIONS OF SERVICE
13.   Student nurses receive free board and lodging and live in the nurses' home or where else required. Indoor uniform, together with laundry (up to 24 articles per week) is provided.
        Salary is paid monthly in arrears, beginning from the date of the commencement of training (including any period in the Preliminary Training School) on the following scales:-

---

[3]   The student nurse is responsible for the payment of the Examination Fees of the General
Nursing Council:
Examination fees of the General Nursing Council:
Preliminary Examinations £2–2–0. Final examination £3–3–0.
There are no fees for the Hospital Examinations.

	Salary	Value of Emoluments	Total value Salary and
1st year	£55 pa	£75 pa	£130 pa
2nd year	£65 pa	£75 pa	£140 pa
3rd year	£75 pa	£75 pa	£150 pa
4th year (until State Registered)	£75 pa	£75 pa	£150 pa
5th year (after State Registered)	£95 pa	£75 pa	£170 pa

14.   Student nurses are under the authority of the Matron and are required to obey the instructions of their superior officers and, in professional matters, of the Medical staff. They work in the wards and departments of the Hospital as allocated by the Matron and are required to undertake night duty as directed. At all times when in the wards and departments of the Hospital they shall wear the regulation uniform. As far as is possible a student nurse will remain in the Hospital Unit to which she is primarily appointed, but circumstances may arise in which the transfer to another Hospital Unit may be desirable. (In conditions of emergency existing during the war, nurses may be required to take part of their training at other hospitals as directed by the Nursing Committee).

15.   Student nurses are normally on duty for an average of 96 hours per fortnight, exclusive of meals and inclusive of compulsory lectures.

16.   The periods of weekly off duty and annual leave are as follow:
3 hours off duty daily
1 day off per week
4 weeks' annual leave (in one or more parts).[4]
During annual leave, student nurses will receive, in addition to their salary, an allowance of 15/- per week.

17.   Student nurses' specified hours of study, off duty times and annual leave are adhered to as closely as possible, but are subject to the exigencies of the Hospital's service.

18.   On production of a medical certificate, sick leave with pay, reduced by an amount equivalent to the statutory benefit to which a student nurse is entitled under the National Health Insurance Acts[5], will be granted up to the following periods:

---

[4]   Four weeks annual leave as prescribed by the Rushcliffe Report will be adopted as soon as possible.

[5]   A student nurse who is exempt from Health Insurance on the ground of assured private income shall pay to the Hospital the amount of sickness benefit to which she would have been entitled if she had been insured.
During the first year: 1 month's full pay and (after 4 months' service) two months' half-pay
During the second year: 2 months' full pay and 2 months' half-pay.
During the third year and subsequent years: 3 months' full pay and 3 months' half pay.

If the student nurse is not being provided by the Hospital with in-patient treatment she will receive during the periods of sick leave, in lieu of board and residence, an allowance of 15/- per week, while on full pay, and 7/6 per week, while on half-pay.

19. If the student nurse is unable to resume her duties at the end of the appropriate prescribed periods her engagement will thereupon be deemed to be automatically terminated without notice. The Nursing Committee may, at its discretion, extend the period of sick leave (with or without pay). Any such discretionary payment by the Hospital to the nurse will not create a fresh agreement of employment and training, and may be discontinued at any time without liability on the part of the Hospital to give notice.

20. If a student nurse becomes entitled to any allowance under the Workmen's Compensation Acts, she shall, while remaining in residence, make such payment to the Hospital as the Nursing Committee shall decide.

22. A student nurse wishing to marry is required to give the Hospital one month's notice of her intention and on her marriage her contract as a student nurse will thereby by terminated without prejudice to the renewal of her contract being considered by the Nursing Committee.

23. Any student nurse desiring to break her contract for her personal convenience or giving less than one month's notice of her intention to marry, may be required to pay a forfeit of:
If in the first year of training   £ 6
If in the second year of training   £ 7
If in the third year of training   £ 8
If in the fourth year of training   £10

24. The Matron may suspend a student nurse from duty at any time during her training, reporting the same to the Nursing Committee immediately, and the Nursing Committee may terminate the contract of any student nurse at any time without notice for neglect of duty, disobedience, misconduct or other sufficient cause.

Nurses involved in this project remembered the first 6–12 weeks of the 4 year SRN Course were spent in the Preliminary Training School (PTS) Southfield. In the early 1940's, the working school day was long with breakfast at 7.15 a.m. and not officially ending until 8.30 p.m. This was later shortened at both ends of the day. Before classes began these new student nurses had daily cleaning tasks to do until the mid 1960's, involving their bedrooms and the school rooms.

Sister Tutors of the 1940's and 1950's dictated lectures to the PTS student nurses on a range of subjects including anatomy, physiology, hygiene; these were taken down and for many years the books were assessed by the Sister Tutors.

Teaching methods were dogmatic and one learnt mostly by rote.

After a few weeks, wearing unflattering green gowns, these new student nurses spent some very formative hours on the wards, where they learnt and saw much. Also during these weeks outside visits were made to a dairy, the Sewage works in connection with hygiene lessons and Oozells Street School for invalid cookery classes.

Towards the end of the preliminary period, written, oral and practical examinations were taken. Failure in any was very serious, resulting in the possible discontinuation of training. At the end of the PTS one nurse remembered a type of 'Passing out Parade' in which they proudly wore their new uniforms, and displayed their new skills and entertained parents to tea.

It was noted previously that in early 1943, QEHNTS became one of the first training school in the country to institute the Block system. This involved two groups (PTS) of student nurses coming into school once yearly for an intensive period of theoretical instruction (and much enjoyed physical rest) lasting 4–6 weeks. Unfortunately (and in common with many other schools subsequently) the content of subject material in the Study Block rarely matched subsequent ward experience, so learning was still rather unconnected. Nurses remembered the allocation to hospital wards being a somewhat haphazard experience until 1949 when Miss Thould was appointed as Assistant Matron to the QEH to take charge of the allocation system, another initiative of Miss Smaldon's. Allocation to wards was clearly still driven by service needs, (i.e. the need to ensure there were enough nurses to care for the patients), but this did improve remarkably. Prior to that student nurses could spend any time between 9 weeks and 3 months on one ward area, and little note appeared to be taken of previous experience. Thus a student nurse could spend a long period on one ward e.g. neurology and then be sent to a neurosurgical ward for another block of three months – hardly a balanced programme given the range of medical conditions. Other experience was gained in the maternity ward (East 4) and there was usually one student nurse sent for clinical experience to the nurse's sick bay – this was often a student nurse who was herself in post convalescence experience as this was seen as a 'light allocation'!

Once on the wards, student nurses in 1939–1942 came back to the classroom for more formal lectures or demonstrations not only from their Sister Tutors but also from QEH senior medical staff. These happened always in the nurses' off duty whether on day or night duty and lasted about 1–2 hours only, so learning was very disjointed.

Experience was also acquired in the operating theatres where a nurse who had this allocation in 1954 remembered the work evolving around preparation of equipment needed for operations, cleaning it afterwards and sterilising it in

Nurse Jennifer Clarke (30th PTS) in theatre

the steriliser and water boiler and intensive use of Lysol, a 'pungent caustic substance' used to sterilise sharp instruments such as needles and blades. Sutures and hypodermic needles were inspected after every use for damage by drawing the point through cotton wool; if it snagged that it was put on one side for re-sharpening. New needles were rarely available! Surgical gloves were washed in soapy water tested for leaks and, if found patched up! They were then put into pairs in a linen envelope with a talcum powder ball, packed in a drum and autoclaved. Large chest 'mops' were washed, hung to dry and then re-sterilised and re-used.

THE QUEEN ELIZABETH HOSPITAL

EXPERIENCE CHART

NAME   *Nurse Marian Elsie Powell.*

ENTERED   *A.K. January. 194 9.*

The Sister, as she teaches the nursing points mentioned in the left-hand column, is requested to mark the same in the column descriptive of her Ward—Surgical, Medical, etc. One stroke indicates that the Nurse has been shown, but is not proficient in the detail. A cross must only be given when both the Sister, and the Student Nurse herself, are satisfied that a high standard of proficiency has been attained. The Sister placing a cross will insert her initials in the right-hand column, using as little space as possible.

This Chart must be deposited in the Matron's Office at the end of each term.

Front page of Experience book.

EXPERIENCE CHART

JUNIOR STUDENTS

Department	P.T.S.	School	Surgical	Medical	Children	Gynæ-cological	
Domestic Ward Management.							
Method of cleaning	/		x	x	x	x	x
Care of furniture, bedsteads, cupboards	/		x	x	x	x	x
Care of bedding, linen, blankets, mackintoshes	/		x x	x	x	x	x
Care of kitchen, bathroom, lavatory	/		x	x	x x	x	x
Sanitary methods of cleaning utensils, baths, lavatories, crockery	/		x	x	x	x	x
Disposal and disinfection of soiled linen and dressings	/		x	x	x	x	x
Bedmaking.							
General	/		x x	x x	x x	x	x x
Special for Operation	/		x	x x	x	x	x
Fracture	/		x				
Plaster	/						
Amputation	/				x		
Rheumatism	/				x x		
Renal	/						
Cardiac	/		x x	x x	x x	x x	x x
Lifting of patients and care of pressure points	/		x x	x	x x	x	x x
Management of patients after operation	/		x x	x	x x	x	x x
Filling hot water bottles	/		x	x	x		
Filling water pillows and beds	/		x	x			
Filling air pillows and beds	/		x	x	x x	x	x x
Receiving new patients	/		x x	x	x	x	x x
Bathing in bed and bathroom	/		x	x			
Combing and washing of heads	/		x	x	x x	x	x x
Care of hands and feet	/		x	x			x
Care of mouth	/		x x	x		x	x x

First signed up page of Experience book.

Links with the medical school

In the autumn of 1944 a special arrangement was made with the Professors of Anatomy and Physiology at the Medical School. For many years, they and their colleagues gave stimulating erudite lectures, demonstrations, and laboratory experiments to generations of QEH student nurses. The medical school staff also set and marked examination papers and conducted oral examinations at that time. The first group to have this experience even had their hands and shoes inspected by Miss Woodhouse before going to the Medical School!

All through the years, and during every allocation, student nurses learnt nursing skills and knowledge by repetition and example, being watched over by more senior student nurses, staff nurses and sisters. In addition they acquired the arts of making patients comfortable, observing and assessing their conditions and progress.

Having achieved competency in each of a huge range of procedures (kaolin poultices, non-touch dressing techniques, bed bathing, fluid balance charting, caring for pressure areas, giving and checking drugs, injection technique, giving enemas etc.) sister had to tick the appropriate place in the individual nurses' Experience Book'. This book had to be taken to the State Final Practical Examination, so was important.

Qualifying as a nurse

Once the nurse successfully completed her Final State Examination at the end of three years she qualified as a State Registered Nurse. The fourth year of the course was spent as a junior staff nurse, learning and practising the techniques of ward management and those of now teaching nursing to the next generation of student nurses.

Prize days

Prize days were seen as important transition in the nurses career, the day in which the hard work of training was acknowledged and celebrated. Prizes, such as gold and silver medals were awarded but these were not competitive but given on the basis of the nurse's progress through her training. The first nursing staff prize day was held in 1943 and the President of the General Medical Council presented the prizes. On the platform with him was Dame Elizabeth Cadbury supported by the Chairman of the Board and the House Committee. No mention is made of Matron or Sister Tutor. Indeed, although a Nursing Advisory Committee was extant from 1935, no nurse was listed as a member until the new structure was initiated with the advent of the NHS in 1948.

Prize giving 1948 – Matron (Miss Smaldon) looks on as Doreen Tennant is presented with silver medal.

In 1946 Aneurin Bevan, Minister of Health, presented the nurses' prizes and in 1947 Mr. B. J. Ward, a Genito Urinary Surgeon. It is interesting to note his family had instituted the Bernard Ward Prize for Male Nurses. In 1952, The Nurse's Prize Day had as guest of honour Professor Thomas Bodkin of the Barber Institute of Fine Art, and in 1953 Miss Kathleen Chesney, Principal, Westfield College, University of London. The Challice family gave the Leslie Eaton Challice Prize for a Male Nurse in memory of Leslie E. Challice, Chief Technician in Bacteriology and Clinical Pathology, having given 32 years service (As noted in Chapter 1, Mr. Challice was one of the members of staff who had moved from the Queen's Hospital).

An illustration of the nature of the events at prize giving in 1953 can be seen in Figure 3.3. it should be noted that prize giving was held in the Recreation room of Nuffield house (the Rec) until 1956 and from 1957 the event was moved to the University of Birmingham Great Hall.

Figure 3.3
Programme for Annual Prize Giving November 1953

THE UNITED BIRMINGHAM HOSPITALS
QUEEN ELIZABETH HOSPITAL

ANNUAL PRESENTATION OF MEDALS AND PRIZES

Friday 6th November, 1953 at 3.0 p.m.
in the Main Hall of Nuffield House

Mr. T.A. Hamilton Baynes, M.A., J.P. presiding

Mr Hamilton Baynes, Chairman of the House Committee, Queen Elizabeth Hospital, will extend a welcome to Miss K. Chesney, D. Litt (Oxon)., and to the Nurses and their parents and friends.

The Matron , Miss C. A. Smaldon, will give the twelfth annual report on the Queen Elizabeth Hospital Unit of the Queen Elizabeth School of Nursing.

Miss Chesney, D.Litt. (Oxon)., will present the Gold and Silver Medal and other prizes and Hospital Certificates of Training.

Miss Chesney will address the meeting.

Nurse S.J. Light, the Gold Medallist will propose a vote of thanks to Miss K Chesney and Mr T.A. Hamilton Baynes.

Nurse M.I Taylor, the Silver Medallist, will second the vote of thanks.

—000—

1946–50 Changes across the Birmingham United Hospitals

To meet the demands of the training programme set by the GNC there was a need to gain clinical experience in other specialities not available at that time at the QEH.

During these four years it became a requirement of the GNC that student nurses had a practical paediatric allocation at the Children's' Hospital, and the 24th. PTS were the first group to spend 8 weeks there. Many student nurses found this a distressing experience, but somewhat eased by the availability of real dripping in the dining room! The young patients were quiet and subdued, perhaps because they were allowed no visitors and could not wear their own clothes. Nursing sick children was upsetting and even worse when their condition was life threatening. One nurse vividly recalled an 'awful, sad meeting of parents carrying their obviously dead baby', whom she had to lay out, and then take with the parents to the Chapel, a very dreadful experience, which has stayed in her memory. Other memories exstudent nurses had were of washing already matted and shrunk woollies in 'the awful sluices' for use by their patients, in the knowledge that *"Sister had lots of new woollies locked away in her cupboard"*.

During these weeks they recalled remembered living in a 'very chilly' house called Bushwood and having to revert to the 'old pattern of off duty', as the shift system had not been introduced.

Some students went to the Midland Nerve Hospital which at that time had neurological patients (although later it was changed to care of people with mental health problems) and many student nurses felt ill prepared to care for them as, for them, it was obviously a strange and rather frightening experience. Others, however, had more positive memories.

Student nurses were required to have a gynaecological nursing allocation either at QEH on East 4A or at the Women's' Hospital, and this was a fairly happy time, although on night duty they seemed to do little else but make and cut stock to pack the piles of empty dressing drums.

1951–55 In the classroom
After those initial months of theoretical training, student nurses spent four to six weeks yearly in Study Blocks in Nuffield House. Here the school rooms included a big classroom, which later became the Staff Nurses sitting room, on the ground floor and two small classrooms and the wooden tiered lecture theatre on the Lower Ground Floor. Nursing procedures were demonstrated and practised in a 'practical room' until perfection was achieved by all.

When student nurses were in study block suitable visits were also arranged. The first year Block went to the Medical School for lectures and demonstrations in Anatomy and Physiology given by the professors or senior lecturers. The Professor of Anatomy was a 'rather fearsome character'. Sadly at this time, the GNC Syllabus of Training was in need of updating, and this meant that some out of date procedures had to be learnt, for example, 'cupping', the use of hot cups to 'draw a boil' and the use of leeches to suck blood. Also it was noted that it was still not possible to match the Study Block content closely to subsequent or previous practical experience, (this was not achieved for another 15 years).

Undoubtedly in PTS and in Study Block student nurses were shown the ideal

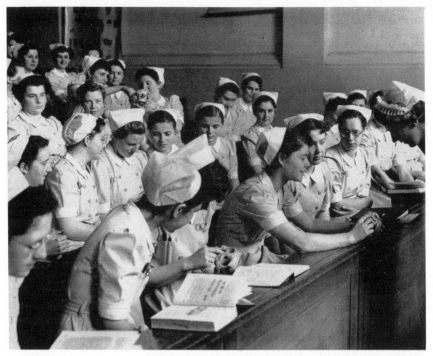

Student nurses and Principal Tutor Miss M. Bomford in the tiered lecture theatre in Nuffield House.

ways of preparing and carrying out procedures. On the wards they were pressurised and 'corners had to be cut'. Teaching methods involved much 'talk and chalk'. The seating in the cold Lecture Theatre was very uncomfortable, so many brought rugs and hot water bottles! For some time the student nurses had to sit in alphabetical order!. However these periods away from shift work and the wards allowed batteries to be recharged, and all had extra energy to enjoy evenings off duty, a luxury indeed.

Sister Tutors remembered included Miss Woodhouse, the first Principal Tutor, Miss Bomford who was seen as 'an excellent teacher of theory and practice'. Miss Whiter and Miss Thould were both 'much loved' and Miss Lawson was seen as a 'strict Scottish lady' Miss McLennon who was 'held in awe'. In the 1950's nurse remembered the tutelage of Miss I. Parnell who was much admired and very clever, always stimulating her charges, also Miss M. Reed and Miss C.Snee.

The end of the Queen Elizabeth Hospital Nurse Training School

The King agreed to the naming and foundation of Queen Elizabeth School of Nursing involving the amalgamation of the three training schools within the new United Birmingham Hospitals, the group of hospitals that emerged after the NHS (see Chapter 5) but it took many years for this to be fully implemented. This agreement was noted in a letter from the Home Office in the minutes of the Board of Governors on the 10 Febraury 1950.

On March 11th. 1955 the Board of Governors agreed to the appointment of Miss Smaldon as the Chief Nursing Officer of the United Birmingham Hospitals and Principal of the new QESN. As indicated in the previous chapter, Miss Smaldon ceased to be Matron of Queen Elizabeth Hospital to fulfil this role.

Queen Elizabeth Hospital

Chapter 4

Nursing at the Queen Elizabeth Hospital (1938–45)

The Queen Elizabeth Hospital (QEH) opened in 1938 and the first years were remembered not only because of the experience of nursing in a new hospital but because of the occurrence of the Second World War at that time. This chapter will consider not only the first years of the QEHNTS but, in focusing on the time period 1938 to 1945, memories of nursing in QEH during the war will be included.

Nurses Lives 1938–1945
On 4th. October 1938, some three months before the Centre Hospital received patients, 37 young ladies who were to be members of the of the first Preliminary Training School (PTS) arrived at the Nurses Home, Nuffield House, ready to start their career as nurses. At that time Nuffield House was the domain of the stern Home Sister, Miss E. Collett. Once the students had paid their £5 entry fee, they were shown to their individual rooms.

These 'young ladies' remembered spending the first three months of the four year course leading to the qualification of State Registered Nurse (SRN), receiving instruction from their strict, but fair, Principal Tutor Miss E. Woodhouse. Classes included topics in anatomy, physiology, hygiene and, of course, in the theory and practice of nursing. The nurses remembered being expected to practice nursing skills repeatedly until Miss Woodhouse was totally satisfied with their performance and knowledge. This was not easy as she set high standards and was seen as *"a perfectionist"*. A series of cookery classes were held at a school in Oozells Street, to help the students manage the special diets for patients. Some visits were made to the wards wearing 'green gowns' by way of a uniform. In addition these nurses remembered going to visit the Cadburys site, and to the General Hospital to see its Plenum ventilating system.

By 31st. December 1938, after a short holiday for this first group of students, the very first patients were being admitted to the completed wards at QEH. These included the wards of East 1 (East 1A and B) a 60 bedded medical unit run by Sister Turpin and West 3 a 34 bedded surgical ward with Sister Westbrook in charge.

These new student nurses were the first to wear the very unusual nurses

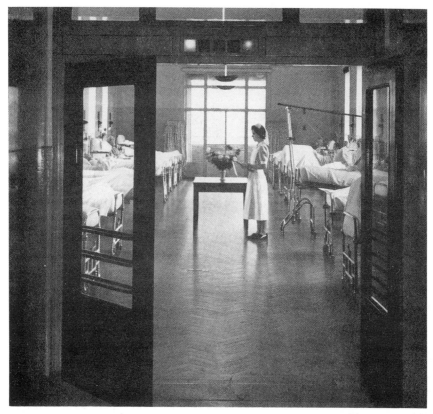

Picture of 16 bedded main wards at QEH. Note lights above doors used as a 'call' system for hospital staff using a system of colour coding.

uniform described in Chapter 3. This avant-garde uniform caused doctors to call the nurses *"The Chorus Girls"*!

On the wards, the student nurses had to work fast and hard with a staff nurse from whom they learned how to nurse. Every morning patients had their hands and faces washed, beds made and breakfast eaten, before Matron Bowes, and her dog, a red setter called Adolf (!) and the doctors' undertook their 'rounds' at about 9 a.m. (The ward round is the term allocated by tradition to the daily visits made to ward areas by senior medical and nursing staff who went round the ward seeing each patient in turn.)

Memories of work on the ward included a 'lot of cleaning of bedsteads, lockers, sluice' although the floors were not included, as the ward maids did these. The junior student nurses also remembered being responsible for serving

Student nurses and dieticians: The diet kitchen.

patients with their mid-morning drinks. They were encouraged to watch the staff nurses undertaking more complex care for example giving injections and doing dressings as well as learning nursing skills, such as careful rolling of patients when changing bottom sheets and caring properly for pressure areas. It was rare for a patient to develop a pressure sore; if one occurred it had to be reported to the Matron! (There is little doubt that in those days evidence of a

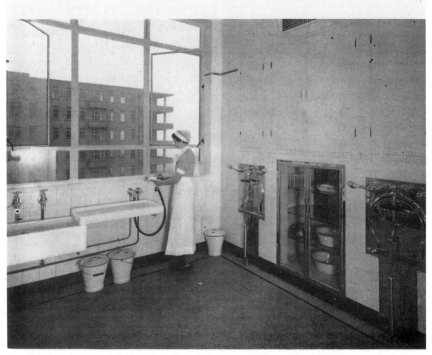

The ward annexe known as the sluice room. Note the stainless steel door behind the nurse that was the bed pan washer – another innovation in the 'state of the art' hospital.

pressure sores was seen as a failure of the nursing care which, given the knowledge developed since that time would indicate that nurses may have been unfairly reprimanded for such an event as, although it is recognised that regular change of position is crucial, it is now known that a number of other factors may contribute towards pressure sore development.)

Another memory of most student nurses was the time spent in the sluice – the domain of junior student nurses! There are many memories of a lot of time spent in the 'upmarket' sluice, where there was much involvement with the bedpan washers and the stainless steel bedpans, as it seemed that all the patients were bedfast. All the linen and rubber sheets soiled by incontinent patients had to be sluiced, then put on a clothes horse out on the sluice balcony to dry. At the end of the day all the dirty laundry had to be folded and put into separate piles for counting, before being 'bagged' (put into linen bags) for transfer to the laundry via the chute. (The chute was another innovatory part of the QE Hospital design. This consisted of long narrow tunnels in the east and west blocks that passed from the top to the bottom of the hospital with access point at each ward guarded by a heavy metal door that was just big enough to take the filled laundry bags.) As the laundry bags from all wards were dispatched by these chutes this enabled an efficient laundry collection service from two central points at ground level thus representing quite a manpower saving.

The hours of duty for these student nurses during the early years of the QEH were from 7 a.m. to 9 p.m. with time off during the day, either from 10 a.m. to 1 p.m., or 2–5 p.m. or an evening off from 5.30 p.m. and there was one day off weekly. Not surprisingly with all this labouring, the students were always hungry; good food was available- supplemented with buns!

Whilst this group of students remember with happiness the delayed visit of the King and Queen and renaming of the hospital in March 1939, such memories are marred by the fact that six months later, Great Britain and France were at war with Germany and this was to have a big impact on nursing in QEH during years to come. In June 1940 the nurses and hospital had to cope with several hundred wounded military personnel evacuated in little ships from the beaches at Dunkirk. On the special military wards, the nurses remembered the men were very well looked after. This care included a barrel of beer available for them in the ward kitchen! Once they felt better they helped out, for example by cleaning the nurses shoes until they shone like patent leather. Particular memories of night duty were the long hours (9 p.m. to 8.15 a.m.) and remembering that during the air raids the city could be seen in flames. These raids injured 6500 and killed 2200 citizens. Despite all this trauma and hard work, time was found for illicit quick 'fry-ups' in the kitchen at 2 a.m., whilst the senior nurse was at mealbreak! Night nurses were expected to do their share of bed baths and bed making before going off duty, even if this involved staying late on the wards.

The nurses who were in training then still recall vividly the firing of Anti-Aircraft guns based in the fields behind Nuffield House, hearing the rattle of shrapnel on the steel blinds covering the big windows in Theatre 1 and 2, and of swimming in the static water tanks (stored for fire fighting) outside East Lower Ground. The student nurses slept in siren suits either on straw palliases or on their mattresses in the Crush Hall on the lower ground floor of Nuffield House, during air raids. At 6 a.m., they went upstairs to dress and go on duty.

Throughout these experiences theoretical training continued with lectures given by senior doctors, usually in off duty time, on medical, surgical matters and speciality subjects (neurology, ear, nose and throat, ophthalmics, gynaeco-logy). After about 18 months there was the General Nursing Council (GNC) Preliminary Examination (see Chapter 3) to be taken. As it was necessary to pass these examination to progress on the nursing training programme, they created a lot of stress. At this time the QEH could not host the practical part of the examination and so students had to attend a strange hospital, with different equipment, thus making it even more stressful.

Social life
During training the student nurses social life was of course limited, not only by the dreadful war conditions, but by the small annual remuneration received (£18 for first year, £20 for second year, £25 for third year and £30 for fourth year). At this time however, they were not charged for their accommodation, food or laundry.

Initially there was no bus service and the nurses either walked to the nearby village of Harborne or through the University to the Bristol Road, a main road leading to the city centre. The rules were strict and student nurses had to be back by 11 p.m. at Nuffield House unless they had a late pass.

The tennis courts were remembered as a 'late arrival' for this group but they did recall the occasionally dances or hops in Nuffield House.

Christmas was made as special as possible for staff with a Christmas show and dinner; at each place was a box of Cadbury chocolates and a packet of Woodbines! It is important to remember not only were the staff financially impoverished but so was the hospital. It was still a voluntary hospital (see Chapter 1), with the almoner collecting money on a means test basis from the patients. Donations were always gratefully received.

At times, nurses became ill and patients themselves in Sick Bay which was on the first floor of Nuffield House. There the sick nurses were "*treated marvellously*". Septic fingers were a frequent painful problem (surgical gloves were not available on the wards then to help avoid such problems). There were no antibiotics, but sulphonamides had been available since about 1938. Pulmonary tuberculosis was a common British disease, some nurses succumbed and a few sadly died. A key memory of that time was that after their arrival Professor Wynn gave all student nurses a test for tuberculosis, it seems from these memories that the same syringe and needle was used for all although it was hard to substantiate this! The Nurses Sick Bay remained on the first floor of Nuffield House for many years.

Impression of senior staff
Many sisters, staff nurses, senior doctors and surgeons made great impressions on the young student nurses in the early 1940's. Those remembered include Mr. G. Baines (R.S.O.), Sisters Beatrice and Molly Byrne, Staff Nurse Cliffe, Mr. Fulford, Sister Hoggard, Sister Hughes (West 2), Dr. Humphries, Mrs H. Lloyd, Sister Pegler, Mr. Baron Rose, Mr. J. Sankey, Mr. H. Sampson, Mr. R. Scott

Mason, Mr. J. Small, Mr. G. Speakman (Pharmacist), Dr Brian Taylor, Staff Nurse E. Thould, Sister E. Timmington, Mr. B.Ward, Mr. Beckwith Whitehouse, Professor K.D.Wilkinson, and Mr.Musgrave Woodman. These professionals helped mould and prepare student nurses for the GNC Final SRN Examination and their fourth year as junior Staff Nurses wearing the coveted long cap.

Memories of the War

The Second World War had special effect on the QEH not only because of the direct effect of thousands of wounded military personnel and many air raid victims being treated there, but because it was all happening in a new untried hospital; all this made an impact on the vision of the hospital. Additionally the experiences of nursing in a new hospital during those war years resulted in special memories for the nurses interviewed in the course of the project.

On the day after World War 2 began another group of 28 young ladies arrived at Nuffield House, to begin their training programme. They remembered being shown to their individual bedrooms by Sister Tutor Woodhouse in her "*very starched white uniform*". Of these 27 new student nurses just starting their four year course to qualify as SRN's seven were significantly foreigners and included some Jewish women (four from Czechoslovakia. one each from Germany, Austria and USA). This was to have implications in terms of the numbers completing as all the foreign student nurses were temporarily allocated to other hospitals during the critical time in the war.

Whilst these new student nurses were having tea in the dining room, other nurses were busy pasting black paper onto big windows to comply with blackout regulations. They remembered their own first few days spent stuffing hay into sacks to make mattresses and pillows; this being done in a nearby field in perfect weather with much sneezing and drinking of lemonade supplied by Matron Bowes. The mattresses were required for the nurses who would sleep in the Crush Hall in the anticipated air raids.

Some weeks later ten members of this student group were asked to go to Queens Theological College, Somerset Road, to sleep for some weeks. Sadly one of the new student nurses developed diphtheria and was dispatched to the fever hospital and slowly recovered, but did not return to training. Another remembered spending two periods at this chilly fever hospital with German measles and later with mumps.

The nursing leadership in the hospital was to undergo some critical changes in the early months of the war. Matron Bowes married in February 1940 and left in the summer of 1940. In those last few months of her 'reign' several staff nurses were made ward sisters (Miss Jones, Simpson and Spencer etc.); they remember being on duty from 8 a.m. to 5 or 5.30 p.m. and having two days off on alternate weekends. As the Battle of Britain was beginning, on 12th August 1940, Miss C. A. Smaldon the new Matron arrived. Just before this Birmingham experienced its first air raid when a lone bomber released bombs on Erdington. Miss Smaldon was remarkable for those times being only 35 years old, which was young for such a responsible post at such a critical time, but she was full of ideas and developed into a great pioneer of nursing (see Chapter 7).

1st. June 1940 saw the arrival at QEH of the first batch of Dunkirk wounded; they were very stiff, sore and tired, exceedingly filthy having been repeatedly blown off their feet into the mud. Some came by train, which stopped at the bottom of the road from the hospital, others travelled by ambulance from the south coast. They were delivered to the hospital's east end to a ramp used to load and unload the laundry then taken to E.L.G. (which was not a functioning ward, being unfinished and called a carcass ward) before being taken to the wards.

The men arrived still caked in mud and blood in ruined uniforms (more had to be obtained.) and cleaning these caused a lot of work for the nurses. Local people sent in silk pyjamas and dressing gowns, soap, brushes and combs, writing paper and stamps, books and cigarettes etc. for these men. One key memory of that time was that Sister E. Richards, Assistant Matron/Dietician *"always managed to have a hot meal ready for the convoys of casualties'* .

About 200 Dunkirk wounded were received and treated by QEN staff. It was heartbreaking seeing them so severely wounded but heart-warming to see so many recover. All the men were suffering from severe loss of sleep. Many had gunshot wounds having been sitting in the back of lorries shooting and being shot at; guardsmen had bayonet wounds from awful hand to hand fighting; some wounds were very infected. One nurse recalls French stokers with bad burns about their face etc. from when their ship was blown up, and also two nuns whom the soldiers found and brought with them!

Nurses worked from 7 a.m. to 9 p.m. for three days without a break because the wards were so very busy.

The air raid sirens and actual air raids went on almost nightly, (or so it seemed to the exhausted people of Birmingham). The worst air raids included one on 24/25th October 1940 which caused many city centre fires, another on the next night which killed 19 people in a Sparkhill cinema, and 350 bombers came on the 19/20th November 1940 causing injury or death to 1353 people, the devastation of the B.S.A. (Birmingham Small Arms) factory and damage to many water mains, another on the 22/23rd November 1940 when 200 bombers caused 600 serious fires and destroyed more water mains, leaving the city in a perilous state. More air raids followed in December 1940 on the 3/4th. and another on the 11/12th. which lasted 13 hours, more in March 1941 and the last heavy raid was on the 9/10th April 1941 caused serious damage at the General

Hospital and injured or killed 1121 people. Just a few more small raids occurred in the spring or early summer of 1941, but in July 1942 on the 28th and 30th over 900 were killed or injured because ' they failed to take shelter'. The last raid happened on the 23rd. April 1943. (Ballard 1985)

Air raid shelters were built into the banks to the west of Nuffield House. On the top of these banks there evolved allotment type plots tended by some senior nurses one of whom was Miss Woodhouse the Principal Tutor. Some 25–30 years later this area housed the new purpose built QE School of Nursing.

During the autumn of 1940 the air raid casualties poured into Birmingham's hospitals and at QEH the ward nurses were almost over whelmed, so it was arranged that the new student nurses of the 7th. PTS undergoing their three months introductory programme should spend some hours daily in the ward sluices. Air raids caused concern as they were the triggers to cause some asthmatics to have severe attacks.

The many air raids in 1940 and the first few months of 1941, caused havoc for the hospitals of the city. When a land mine and bombs fell in the grounds of the Children's Hospital, the patients were evacuated to Malvern; the Ear, Nose and Throat Hospital was evacuated to QEH.

On occasions, the hospital itself came under attack and during one raid some 90 incendiary bombs landed on the hospital roof. The doctors were up there pushing them to the ground to be extinguished. At this time Mr. Biffen (well known for many years as QEH's Instrument Curator) was an in-patient on West 3; he got out of bed and went to the fire hose by the medicine cupboard and ran it up the main ward, across the balcony and over its edge, to help the fire fighters below. He ran back and turned on the tap, but the hose had perished and the main ward was thoroughly sprayed with much water from many holes and virtually none reached the fires! In those minimal staff days no one had responsibility for hoses, all able bodied men were in the forces. The only part of QEH site to suffer bomb damage was some derelict farm buildings where years later the Sankey garden was created with money left to QEH nurses by Mr. J. Sankey who was a QEH Surgeon.

A junior night nurse on East 1A remembers having a huge work load. This was a very busy male medical ward receiving emergency admissions of ill patients nightly, 'work involved getting drinks, checking drugs, giving Adrenaline to asthmatic attack patients, bed baths,' doing backs', measuring urine, charting fluid balance, answering bells, putting up cot sides, doing bread and butter, (the R.M.O. was especially good at this too!). If the air raid sirens sounded her first duty was to fill the baths and sterilisers, presumably in case the water supply was lost. Another nurse recorded three wounded women in adjacent beds, each had lost their husband, and another lady who had 11 severe

Queen Elizabeth Hospitals' Main Entrance showing X-ray department on the first floor and massage department on the second floor. The third floor was not occupied at this time.

scalp lacerations and a torn iris of her eye.

Until 1941 it was perceived that Britain was 'alone' in the war, but in December that year a major ally and another major enemy were identified, when the USA, navy was attacked by the Japanese at Pearl Harbour. Before many months had passed thousands of GI's were stationed in Britain. In October 1942 after months, even years of no successes, Britain celebrated the successful battle of El Alamein, with the ringing of church bells which had been silent for some years.

During 1943 QEH received small convoys of wounded Allied and other soldiers from the North African campaigns. A night nurse remembers a ward full of prisoners, Germans one side, Italians the other side. The latter were terrified of the Germans. Another nurse had the job of 'specialling' (i.e. caring on a 1 to 1 basis) a SS German prisoner with very badly damaged legs; he had been educated at Oxbridge but she felt he 'was a beastly man' telling her what Germany would do to Britain when they conquered it. He believed his morphine injections were intended to kill him. Outside his single room were two armed soldiers guarding him and his nurse! The nurse was thankful when he was out of danger and transferred out of the hospital. In April and May 1943 the 8th army having succeeded in Africa moved to Italy and some dreadfully injured soldiers were brought to the hospital from the awful battles around Monte Cassino.

Early in May 1944 the QEH was ordered to evacuate all its civilian patients, and thereafter only admit civilian emergencies. This was a clue that great things were about to happen. Operation Overlord began on June 6th. 1944 with General Eisenhower broadcasting the official statement at 9.45 a.m. that the invasion had begun. At dinner two days later on the 8th of June, the R.S.O. (Mr. Ted Edwards) announced to the resident doctors that Surgeons (Professor Seymour Barling, Mr. H. Donovan, Mr. H. Sampson, Mr. J. Sankey and Mr. W. Sweet) and their house surgeons were to be ready to receive, assess, and later operate on wounded personnel. Other housemen were to go to bed and sleep, as both nursing and medical staff were to start immediately doing very abnormal shifts. 8 hours on, 8 hours off duty 8 hours on etc. By 10 p.m. that evening it was confirmed that a convoy of 216 patients was on its way by train. It stopped at Selly Oak station and speedily unloaded one patient every thirty seconds who were brought to QEH by coach, lorry or ambulance. A notice displayed in the front hall:-

Convoy expected	216 patients
Time expected	8.6.44. 11–15 p.m.
Convoy arrived	9.6.44 2.00 a.m.

However the majority of these patients were not wounded from the D-Day beaches but evacuated from Portsmouth Hospital where the most seriously wounded D-Day wounded had taken their place. At Gosport Lt. Col. R. K. Debenham and Lt. Col. A. Kerr saw over the next weeks 17260 casualties, sorted the priority cases and sending many of them to Birmingham. Three convoys on the 10th, 12th, 13th June brought the total of some 520 wounded soldiers to QEH, amongst these were some 80 German POW's. Nurses were sad to find that many of the latter were only 15–16 years old, very frightened and certain that food was poisoned; nurses had to eat a little to convince them. A nurse who spoke German did some useful translating. These convoys of wounded initially arrived almost every 24 hours, but gradually less frequently but continued for the next 7–8 months. Gradually civilian patients returned to some wards. Doctors and nurses became very exhausted by the 8 hours shifts, but still cared for the 'brave wonderful men' who were initially very quiet, even silent, sleeping for much of every 24 hours. After about 4 weeks, the awful 8 hours shifts ceased perhaps due to many nurses becoming ill. One nurse noted:

"I recall also that strange week when we did 8 hours on duty and then had just 8 hours off duty. This meant for me, laying all the breakfast trays on East 3A (I think) about 10.30 p.m. knowing that it would be myself giving them out at breakfast time, soon after coming on duty at 7.00 a.m. the next day! Anyway the powers-that-be decided this rota just wasn't workable – thank goodness ".

On the 50th aniversary of D-Day in 1994, Doreen Tennant went in search of theatre records to prepare an article for the QEHNL magazine and she noted *"After quite an adventurous jaunt, akin to a treasure hunt, I ended somewhere between the now defunct QEH Laundry and the Boiler House, two floors below ground level, in an eerie huge gloomy dirty room, on my own, searching through very old dusty Theatre Registers! I wanted to discover the numbers of military patients who went to QEH theatres for operations in June 1940 (Dunkirk) and during the last six and a half months of 1944 (D-Day and beyond)"* She found that in 1944 the QEH admitted 6670 civilians and 5696 military patients and the details of the theatre registers from 1944 are printed in Figure 4.1.

QEH retained long stay military patients certainly until the end of the war, especially those known as 'the spines ' (those with serious back injuries) who were known and loved by many nurses. To accommodate all these extra patients for these many months 30 bedded wards at QEH now held 50 beds, the Army having supplied narrow Army beds, linen and little lockers.

There were many stories that could be told about these wounded men. There were Scottish soldiers who took their kilts to Normandy, got wounded, brought their kilts with them to QEH where they had to be carefully spread on newspaper under their beds! There were stories of how tanks exploded, burning the soldiers

Figure 4.1
Details of Theatre Registers QEH 1944

Theatres	1	2	3	4	5	Grand Total
Actual numbers:						
10.6.44 to 24.7.44	–	150	–	–	–	
10.6.44 to 31.12.44	494	–	744	693	–	
Estimated numbers:						
25.7.44 to 31.12.44	–	390*	–	–	–	
10.6.44 to 31.12.44	–	–	–	–	590*	
Number of Prisoners of War	14	10*	7	11	10*	
TOTAL	*508*	*550*	*751*	*704*	*600*	*3113*

(*Estimates as Registers not available.NB: Registers for ENT and Ophthalmic Theatres were not inspected.)
(From QEHNL Magazine 1994).

inside 'most awfully'. Then there was the young officer, in the new Airborne Regiment who spent 48 hours in 'No-Mans land' receiving extra wounds during the long hours of the Battle of Arnhem. After the debacle at Arnhem in September 1944 some of the survivors, included the injured glider pilots as well as wounded paras arrived. Another inspiring memory was of a 'brave little wounded chaplain' who pushed a fellow wounded officer in his bed to East 4B to see a new born baby; his wife had just been delivered many miles away!

One nurse vividly remembered her first night duty in June 1944, *"when we sometimes had long eerie blacked out empty wards to look after; waiting for the arrival of convoys of wounded, and the rush when they did"*. Certain wards were set aside for the officers and many more for the other ranks.

There were of course amusing incidents also. For example, by the end of June 1944 the hospital was running out of soap and toilet articles, so the House Governor put a very small ad. in the local newspaper published at 5 p.m. asking if people would bring in a few extra bars of soap for the boys. The result was that *'within an hour another invasion had begun, it still goes on. The hospital has received several tons of soap. Everywhere you go, you smell soap'* Storing the soap became a problem!

Most of the patients recovered remarkably fast from their injuries and were very fond of teasing the student nurses. As the atmosphere was rather formal and strict in those days, with no first names being used, and with a threat of being sent to Matron for minor offences, this served to lighten the atmosphere. It was recognised that the pressure on the student nurses was great and they were given huge responsibilities beyond their years and experience. However a wonderful team spirit prevailed on the wards between both medical and nursing staff at all levels.

As soldiers improved and recovered they were allowed to wear their Hospital Blues, these were blue battle dresses to be worn when up in the wards and on visits outside the hospital. In them the soldiers were able to go to local hostelries and shops, use public transport etc. all for free. Sometimes they returned a little the worse for liquor, especially the wealthier officers who did not wear the Blues!

In the autumn of 1944 the black out restrictions were relaxed and gradually even the 'brown out' faded away. Slowly the Allies in Europe cleared France, Belgium and Holland and conquered the Nazis. Eventually the river Rhine was crossed in March 1945 and the Allies were in Germany. On the 8th May 1945 Germany capitulated and that day was V.E.Day. Victory in Europe. Nurses had an extra day off and there were street bonfires and other celebrations which they attended. In August 1945 Japan surrendered after suffering 2 atomic bomb attacks. August 15th was V.J.Day and the QEH nurses had another welcome extra day off. At last the war was over; the final, official, end date being 2nd September 1945.

Some aspects of nursing care
Patients in the hospital wards were very dependent, being bedfast for weeks rather than days, and required maximum support, e.g. post operative appendicectomy patients were not able to wash themselves until their sutures had been removed. This meant that there was a lot of personal nursing to do. Nurses had to learn how to move patients carefully in bed to change sheets and treat pressure areas. Technical advances were bringing new approaches to care. For example, until 1944 there was no Penicillin, (the first antibiotic) so efforts to control infection included spreading sulphonamide cream onto rolls of lint and storing this in boxes for later use on wounds. When penicillin came only the military patients were allowed to be given it. To be effective about 5cc's were given by intra muscular injections; this was done at 3 hourly intervals as it was a short lasting and rather 'dilute' drug. As a result it was dreaded and hated by those at the receiving end despite its life saving properties. Blood transfusions were fairly rare procedures and few intravenous infusions were done, although rectal infusions were quite common place. Developments in technology continued throughout the war and during this time the wonderful intravenous anaesthetic Pentathol arrived, this was vastly superior to previous methods of inducing anaesthesia.

The living conditions

By September 1941 it had become necessary for student nurses in training to share bedrooms, so the divan beds were replaced by bunks. During air raids nurses took their mattresses to the Crush Hall, this area became the shop in the 1950's, but at this time the shop/post room was a miniature affair on the right as one entered Nuffield House. The night nurses slept in Queens College, a 15 minutes tiring walk or cycle ride often during an evening air raid. One night a bomb fell close to these night nurses quarters and they had great difficulty retrieving their belongings. Thereafter they slept in Emergency Medical Service (E.M.S.) beds on East 5B. which was empty at the time; these beds occupied or unoccupied, regularly folded in half if they had not been correctly fastened, resulting in some disturbed sleeping patterns!

Despite all the privations of the six war years nurses had much fun in Nuffield House. There was a thriving Dramatic Society in which Matron was greatly involved, Tea Dances, and American soldiers invited nurses, including Matron and her Assistants to their dances at their north Birmingham camp, sending transport to Nuffield House for them. They of course came to the dances in Nuffield House. The tennis courts were well used, and there were rough mixed sex hockey matches in a nearby field. As with other years Christmas was a very enjoyable time even in war time at QEH where staff 'made the most of what resources we had.' Moreover, as can be seen in the extract from Cathleen Elliott who was in nurse training during the war years, other ways of socialising are identified.

NURSING IN WORLD WAR II
a personal memory Cathleen Elliot (5th PTS)
(from QEHNL Magazine 1992)

Having just joined the Red Cross, I spent the first Sunday of the war in the Boardroom of Barnsley Hall Hospital learning how to pad a splint. This hospital became part of the Emergency Medical Service and we spent the next three months cleaning and making endless beds, first with straw palliasses and then with horrible army mattresses, for the air raid casualties which did not appear immediately but did later. We filled about 250 stone hot water bottles daily – what a lot of hot water we wasted!

As we were not getting any practical experience we were sent to Bromsgrove Cottage Hospital for a few days to learn how to do a blanket bath, etc. By the end of 1939 we had five patients and a staff of 65! At this point I got permission to apply to QEH to do my training. Very nervously I attended QE for my interview with Miss Bowes. QEH

---

had been open for a year and it was a clean and splendid building. Miss Bowes was a very charming and dignified lady who did her ward rounds with her well trained red setter called Adolf. Alas, one Saturday morning during my early weeks in PTS, Miss Bowes married her Bank Manager and was promptly sacked by the House Committee!! Times have thankfully changed! Miss Smaldon was an admirable successor.

We were measured for our uniform and bent our knees a bit so that our skirts were a little more than the regulation 15 inches from the floor. I recall being very annoyed at having to pay 21/- for my uniform shoes; before then I had never paid more than 14/- for a pair! We also had to buy six pairs of mercerised lisle stockings which I made last 6 years with much darning. Our pay was £18 for the first year, £22 for the second year, and £30 for our third year. Staff Nurses received £50 and Sisters £75. My first month's pay was £1 7s 6d.

The first three months of 1940 I spent living in Queen's College (which had been, and is now again, a Theological College). There were 43 of us and we were a mixed bunch; some were graduates, most had come straight from school, and some had done a bit of nursing. Of the 43 only about 27 stayed the course.

On our first day Sister Tutor (who talked very quietly so we had to listen hard, write down all she said and hand in our notebooks for her correction) gave us a valuable lecture on 'Personal Hygiene' and 'How to behave in Public'. We were told that we must shave our axillae every week and use a good deodorant (how I wish this was more widely taught nowadays). We were told we must never talk about patients, especially not on buses, etc!

The hospital was new, magnificently clean and polished, with lovely big windows and open balconies. Sadly, enormous heavy wooden shutters with brown felt around the edges had to be put up nightly.

About Easter 1940 we started on the wards; I recall being told by a fierce St. Thomas's Staff Nurse "Are you naturally slow?" By early June 1940 lots of extra beds were crammed onto the wards in readiness for the Dunkirk casualties who came to QEH by train, which stopped at the bottom of the road and they were carried to QEH on stretchers. I remember the smell of dirty feet and 'sweet pus' (it used to be called laudable pus, as it was good and showed that the white blood corpuscles were doing a proper job eating up the infection). In 1940, of course, there were no antibiotics; we only had the sulphonamides (M & B 693) and there was a strict rule that nothing containing sulphur (eggs, onions, aspirin etc.) should be given to patients on these drugs. I was nursing a patient who was dying with bronchopneumonia and being treated with M & B693, and a friend bought him the then wonderful gift of an egg. I unthinkingly made him a lovely egg flip and he really enjoyed it. Just as he was wiping the froth from his mouth, the terrifying but much respected Sister Turpin swept in and said "Nurse, what have you given that man?" I told her and she bluntly replied "If that man dies it will be largely your responsibility!"

Penicillin came next. It was grown in jam jars at Hollymoor Hospital and had to be given every three hours. I had a badly infected thumb and amputation was considered; as a civilian I could not have penicillin and was off sick for 7 weeks.

The wards were only designed for 30 patients, but there were many extra army beds and often half the ward complement were military patients. They were allowed to go to town, wearing their 'Hospital Blues'. They kept us well supplied with Woodbines. As night nurses we had to know all the patients' names and diagnoses by the time Night Sister came round. I remember telling Sister Byrne that a lady had fractured a femur at Snow Hill station and she snapped back "which platform nurse?" I said "I'm sorry Sister, I don't know". She retorted "Well you should make it your business to know these things!!"

D-Day, 6th June 1944, caused enormous excitement with constant radio news bulletins. Quite soon lots of casualties started to arrive, including some Germans. I knew a little German and had to go to do some interpreting for Prof. Barling. We were shocked by the young age (15–16 years) of some of the Germans; they were terrified of us and sure we would poison them so we had to eat a little of their food before they would touch it! A Londoner arrived with no notes on a stretcher; I could find only a small wound and it turned out he had "lost me ruddy boots, that's all!!"

Around this time we were working 8 hours on and 8 hours off. The 8 off had to include all our eating and sleeping. It was a very difficult system and after about 8 weeks we were all in a bit of a state, so we returned to our usual schedule. This was 7 a.m. to 9 p.m. with 4 hours off during that period and a day off weekly. Night duty was 9 p.m. to 8 a.m. for 12 nights and then 3 nights off. Staff Nurses did not come on till 7.30 a.m. It was sheer hell getting all the bed cases properly bathed in the first hour or so of the day. Those who could help themselves had to be given a bowl of water, etc. Every patient had to have all their pressure points treated (rubbed with soap and water, then methylated spirit, then dusted with talcum powder). If anyone did get a pressure sore it was a real disgrace. This treatment was repeated 4 hourly and bed sores were very rare – unlike today.

On Sunday mornings we had to do what was known as "Inventing the Inventory" when every item on the ward was checked and ticked off in a big book. Items ranged from lockers and mattresses, to egg cups and cutlery. On this day too we had to comb all the patient's hair for nits (except the private patients). If you were in theatres, you had to unscrew and oil all trolley wheels. This can no longer be considered a nursing duty! On theatre nights, time was spent patching rubber gloves, making plaster bandages, rolling wool swabs, cutting and folding gauze dressings.

Long before the USA came into the war, two charming American Neuro-surgeons came to the QEH to help with head injured casualties. The one who stayed longest was Mr. Floyd Barringer and he has written a fascinating account of his years at the QEH. When the US Army came to Birmingham we used to be invited in parties of 15–20 to their dances etc. I recall a Halloween Party at a big old house in Edgbaston where a rather wizened little elderly man was playing the piano and singing "I'm dreaming of a white Christmas" – it was Irving Berlin!

Despite our lack of money we weren't short of entertainment. There were often 'Trade Show' tickets for the cinema and we played a lot of mixed hockey. Occasionally we skated on Bournville boating lake and once on Edgbaston Golf course lake. We even swam for a short time, after dark, in the big static water tank until they oiled the surface (to rid it of mosquitoes) and those QEH bath towels never looked the same again! We cycled everywhere, even during air raids. At the time I did not feel frightened, but was as I vomited later.

As the air raids increased, we had to sleep on the basement floor of Nuffield House, three of us across two army mattresses. One night having not long been off, Matron came at about 10 p.m. saying "I need volunteers . . . ." There was a bad raid on Coventry and soon casualties were pouring in with terrible injuries.

I don't remember when it was that blood transfusion and other intravenous fluids were first given by a needle, but certainly the usual method was by cutting down and tying a glass cannula into a vein, which could not be used again and usually got infected. In my Final nursing exam I had to lay up such a trolley, which was very complicated. The 'Old Dragon' (examiner) started to look critically at my trolley and I realised that I'd forgotten the glass cannula. I took a chance, hid my panic and the dragon did not notice!

It is strange how easy it is to forget the unpleasant experiences and to enjoy recalling the nice ones.

The war had been a tremendous trial for the whole nation and for the new QEH Every commodity gradually became almost unobtainable and to keep a sort of normal life ticking over was very difficult for individuals and for the hospital authorities. Food, clothes, furnishings, paper, furniture, petrol, electricity were all rationed or very scarce or not available. Nothing was needlessly thrown away thrift was a great virtue instilled into every nurse.

Following the end of World War Two, the hospital gradually returned to its civilian role and eventually lost all its military patients. The 'spines' (the people who has suffered back injuries) were the last such patients to leave, having spent years in the QEH and were known and admired by many student nurses, who had given them care.

The Entrance Hall. In this hall is the Foundation Stone laid by H.R.H. the Prince of Wales and also a Bronze Panel recording the opening by H.R.H. the Duke of Gloucester, who deputised for H.M. the King.

Conclusion

Overall the feeling was that nursing at QEH during war-time had a special quality. Nobody minded how hard they worked, or even if they missed their off duty. There was certainly a feeling of "doing one's bit". As a result of the war the building work planned to develop the concept of a central hospital site in Birmingham was never developed but the QEH continued to provide service and the Nurse Training School continued for many years as will be seen in the next chapters.

Chapter 5

Nursing at the Queen Elizabeth Hospital 1945–57

This chapter will focus on that post war period drawing largely on the memories and experiences of nurses who trained and worked at the QE Hospital during this time. The post war years were very important ones in the lives of the staff of QEH. Slowly over the first two and a half years the military patients departed and the hospital achieved once more its voluntary status caring now for only civilian patients. Discussions were taking place and decisions being made locally and nationally about the coming National Health Service. This change would mean the end of all voluntary and local authority hospitals.

The memories of the student nurses of the late 1940's and 1950's are not coloured by war but in other aspects of their experiences a number of similarities with the first groups of students can be seen. Preliminary training continued to begin with some three months in the PTS in Southfield (see Chapter 3). This large house had elegant rooms with lovely parquet floors. In the spacious grounds, there were acres of spring daffodils and in the autumn trees provided beautiful colours. By April 1951, purpose built classrooms, a practical room and offices had been built on the side of the house; these released rooms in the house for their proper purposes as bedrooms and sitting rooms. The house next door, Priorsfield, had been acquired by July 1954 for the student nurses of the General Hospital but initially the two groups were totally separate although this situation changed later as will be seen below.

It was interesting to note that several of the QEH nurses who were interviewed in this project admitted to applying for nurse training specifically because of the recruitment film 'Student Nurse' described in Chapter 3, which was shown many times in every town and city, even being sent to the USA! Also, another development was that in the early 1950's potential student nurses had the opportunity of completing a week of 'work experience' (long before the idea was commonly accepted into the language). This experience including living in Nuffield House and the opportunity to be a part of a ward team, albeit a tiny part. It gave both the potential students and the hospital staff opportunity to make a final decision about suitability for nurse training.

The patients

Many patients came to the QEH from distant places so they had few visitors. Consequently a lot of conversation went on between these lonely patients and their young nurses. Apparently in these years the female patients seemed eager to rest all they could, whilst the male patients having decided that their illnesses were not terminal became very helpful to the student nurses who always had more to do in the time available. Surprisingly one person interviewed stated that she was not too distressed by patients' severe illnesses, but can still remember their names and diagnoses; another vividly and sadly recalled a child with a severe malignant facial disorder.

The wards

The spice and essence for every student nurse was her life on the wards with the patients. There was some difficulty in adapting to a range of ward experiences and changing wards was very stressful as each ward had different routines and procedures to learn, but eventually student nurses learned to adjust to these moves and settled quite quickly into a different environment.

In general the memories of ward areas were of regimented units where high standards were demanded. The work was hard and, as the QEH wards were spacious, the nurse had to walk long distances. The result was that the nurses were always tired and ordinary sleep never was enough!

Overall nursing duties were wide-ranging, usually fairly ordinary and thus sometimes described as "*tedious*" and at times "*very complex*". In those days, patients were in hospital for much longer and spent longer confined to bed, so nurses knew them well, 'tucking-up' rounds and 'back' rounds were remembered with pleasure as nurses had 'hands on, real nursing' contact. However, a sad memory was of a dying patient thanking his nurse for sitting with him. It was rare for nurses to sit with such patients in those far off days.

On early shifts the patients in the main ward had two nurses looking after them, and another two had similar responsibility for the patients in the side ward. At that time the presentation of the patients was seen as important with great emphasis being placed on "*tidying beds and pillows and keeping bed wheels clean and positioned correctly*". Paralysed patients were classed as "*heavy nursing cases*" in that they were totally dependent on the nurses but the student nurses felt they learned a lot from this type of care. Each ward had an orderly and two domestics; these ladies were important members of the team, although they were sometimes strict, but usually helpful and supportive to the young nurses.

At the start of each shift, the nurses identified their own tasks from the 'work list' prepared each day by the Sister or Senior Staff Nurse and generally demonstrating a hierarchy of tasks for junior and senior nurses. As with the previous group of student nurses (see Chapter 4) it was noted the senior nurses did the more 'complex' tasks of dressing wounds and, medicines, etc. whilst the juniors did, for example, bed making, urine testing, a very common chore, involving test tubes, chemicals and Bunsen burners and took place in a "*small smelly room*". Undertaking practical procedures for the first time was a frightening experience, but once done a special assurance quickly developed. One person interviewed recalled sister supervising whilst, for the first time, she gave a patient an enema, one pint of warm soapy water administered via a funnel and tubing.

There is little doubt that some tasks were not skilled nursing tasks in nature, for example, counting cutlery was amongst the tasks delegated to junior nurses! Nurses also remembered it was the junior student nurses task to offer the patients a variety of beverages (hot or cold milk, Cocoa, Bournvita, or Bovril) during the mornings and again in the evenings, and then having to wash the cups and saucers! Other 'junior' tasks included cleaning lockers, hand basins, and cupboards. Meal times tended to be an elaborate ritual with sister or staff nurse presiding over varying degrees of presentation. For example, the private patients had tray cloths on their meal trays, these were made from uniform material and embroidered by the ladies of Queen Elizabeth Linen League. Other patients however, had more standard presentation of meals.

One of the people interviewed said that early in training, she was advised always to have a cloth in her hand as this "*would indicate that she was busy, and that was very importan*t"! She remembers, with horror, the "*white sputum pots and once, cleaning the clinical thermometers by boiling them*"!

Undoubtedly there was much to learn as procedures were highly skilled, and often involved the wearing of protective gowns and masks, choosing correct equipment, sterilising it and laying up the trolley and preparing the patient both mentally and physically. Then the procedure had to be carried out with dexterity and proper adherence to aseptic principles. At the conclusion, the patient was made comfortable and the trolley cleared and cleaned.

Other technical procedures included intramuscular injections which, at QEH, were given into the thigh muscles not into the gluteal muscles as was the practice in many hospitals. This method was apparently the result of a sciatic nerve being damaged many years earlier. One person recalled how she learned how to perform a bladder washout from a sister and this developed into a favourite and satisfying skill, but she also remembers fainting whilst watching a chest aspiration and being rather scared of nursing patients with underwater seal chest drainage, or those having intravenous infusions; her other anxieties included never feeling confident about calculating insulin dosages and worrying having

Student nurse reports to ward sister.

passed a Ryles tube (stomach tube) for the first time; asking herself *"was it in the right place"*? She also remembered being unsure and frightened of nursing a patient with a 'vaginal radium bomb'. It was always a valued experience to join staff nurse on the medicine round and learn about drugs and their actions.

Other skills involved learning the correct usage of the two sterilisers in the tiny sterilising room. (As noted in Chapter 2 this all important room was apparently forgotten by the planners, and the room which became the sterilising room should have been the patients' clothes cupboard!) The big steriliser was used to boil up instrument dishes, receivers and bowls and the small one for instruments, syringes and needles. The latter were not disposable in those days and were regularly sent to the Instrument Curator for re-sharpening.

Practical teaching

The nurses remembered that as student nurses they could be suddenly given important tasks to do without help and with insufficient knowledge. However, whilst always aware of their limitations, nurses felt this system ensured they

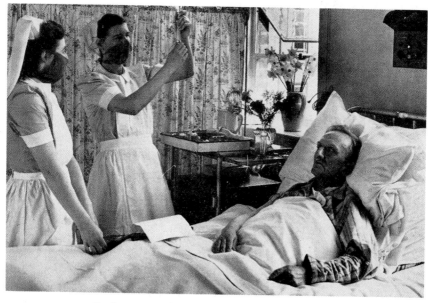

Student nurse being supervised by staff nurse.

quickly become competent! Many still remembered some of the strict instruction of the day, namely that they:–

> "*must not sit on patients beds*", nor "*talk with colleagues across patients*", and they must "*be careful and not wasteful of supplies and equipment*".

Sisters taught their junior student nurses a range of practical and cognitive skills. Some sisters particularly set very high standards and were themselves superb teachers of nursing practise whilst completing the managerial task of ensuring 'smooth running' wards. Undoubtedly there was not enough ward teaching and a lot of learning occurred by watching and copying others and through ones' own mistakes. One noted that learners were shown tray and trolley settings and told about the technique, but not taught how to nurse the patients before, during and after the procedure. Someone else recalled being reprimanded for using an "*incorrect method of swabbing a postnatal patient*", but in her defence she had never received any instruction. This omission was rectified by observing more senior nurses and by their own mistakes, instincts and initiative.

Once the student nurse had achieved proficiency in practical nursing techniques and skills sister allowed the student to put the "*vital tick*" in her

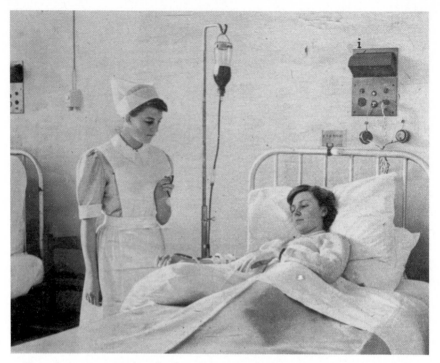

Transfusion in progress. Student nurse checks speed by counting drops per minute. Patient's arm is supported by pillow

student nurses Experience Chart. This was an important document and essential to demonstrate progress at examination time. (See Chapter 3).

Memories of patients
In the late 1940's, there were many long term patients in QEH with open pulmonary tuberculosis and they made a great impact on student nurses. It seemed that in every PTS at least one nurse succumbed to the disease herself. These ill nurses were initially nursed in Sick Bay and then moved to a QEH ward, where they received the best possible medical and nursing care. Streptomycin was the first effective drug, arriving in 1946 but it was initially rather impure, required diluting (so large quantities had to be painfully injected) and toxic, especially to hearing. Para-Amino-Salicylic-Acid was added to this regime. Despite modern therapies the QEH still had some patients with pulmonary tuberculosis well into the 1950's, and their crockery was kept and

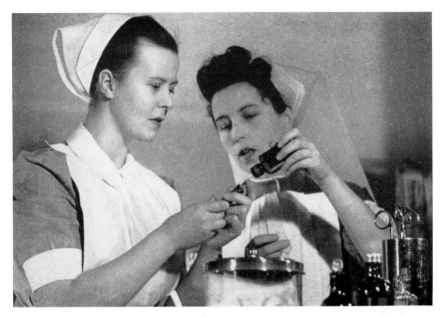

Instruction in the Ward: a staff nurse teaches a student nurse.

cleaned separately in the minute flower room, by the laundry chute; on rare occasions their sputum had to be measured (a much detested task, as was cleaning suction apparatus). The patients spent about 4 months in the QEH before going to a Malvern Hospital to convalesce. Around this time one ex-student nurse still remembers *"dropping a tray of sputum pots"*!

In the early 1950's nurses remembered there was a poliomyelitis epidemic, and Ward East 5A, managed by Sister Brophy was totally given over to barrier nursing these often young, very distressed and ill patients, who put a huge physical, and psychological burden on the nurses. Some patients had respiratory paralysis and two iron lungs were in constant use, others had great pain in their paralysed limbs which had to be carefully splinted. Sadly some patients died. All were in-patients for many months on this well ordered ward. Those who nursed them, can still recall the faces of these patients who made such deep impressions prior to the introduction of the vaccine for polio.

Working conditions
The innovations noted in Chapter 3 were beginning to impact on student lives. The QEH was possibly the first hospital in the country to introduce the shift

system, reducing duty hours to 96 hours/fortnight. (Note that this was seen as an ideal but not possible in the first Annual Report of 1938 (see Chapter 2). The new shift system, seen as "wonderful" by people discussing this memory, was on trial during the autumn of 1946 before being implemented early in 1947. Miss C.Smaldon, the Matron, told her nurses of her wish for them to have their on and off duty in undivided spells. Three shifts covered the 24 hours; early shift ran from 7 a.m. – 4.30 p.m., late shift from 3.30 p.m. – 11 p.m. and night duty from 11 p.m. – 8.15 a.m. It was intended (and expected) that nurses on day duty should have three early and three late shifts weekly, and, of course a day off. On night duty nurses worked 12 nights on duty for two nights off. This new approach was much appreciated.

Night duty

Once a year each group of student nurses spent about three months on night duty with their level of seniority providing some structure to the allocation. They were known as juniors in their first year, middles in the second year and seniors in the third year. Thus it was that each ward had three night nurses with the senior student nurse taking charge of her more junior colleagues. At the start of this period, the nurses worked from 11 p.m. to 8–15 a.m. for twelve nights, then had two nights off duty; but these hours altered to 10 p.m. to 8–15 a.m. for ten nights with four nights off duty during the late 1950's.

During these spells the nurses moved to different accommodation either to the Annexe or to rooms of the fifth floor of the hospital (above the Matron's office). This packing and moving resulted in student nurses becoming later in life, skilled packers of suitcases! All the three night nurses were expected to know the name and diagnosis of every patient on their ward. On occasions a student nurse spent the whole three months acting as relief nurse; covering nurses' nights off for a group of wards. This was not a satisfactory learning experience and certainly very stressful; these relief nurses could be called to special very ill patients, or care for violent patients. Other less onerous work included filling hot water bottles (using a funnel and a cover), cutting and folding stock and packing the dressing drums, ruling up columns in the temperature, pulse and respiration book, and doing other routine non-nursing duties like cleaning sisters office as well as caring for the patients!

Other memories of night duty at this time included cutting and buttering bread for patients' breakfasts, doing lots of clerking, redoing the flowers and much more. But there was fun too – rolling oranges down the corridor from East Ground A to the B side, frying and eating delicious bread fried in arachis oil and, of course, often being caught by senior nurses! There was also the problem of bats! A nurse remembered the night porter coming to remove them with his broom or tennis racket. Clearly they were not a protected species then! The tower water tank overflowed on many occasions necessitating night sister telephoning a very deaf stoker in the boiler room to ask for the valves to be closed in order to restore peace and quiet in the hospital.

Meals were taken during the night in the maid's dining room in the hospital, and the absence of a colleague meant a worrying 30–45 minutes for the two remaining nurses who had to monitor, watch and give patient care with extra vigilance. It was possible to skip a meal break and have a little sleep in the large linen room, on a shelf, which was beautifully warm from the hot water pipes. Needless to say this was not approved of by senior staff!

Memories of Senior Staff

As has been noted in earlier Chapters, Miss Catherine Smaldon was Matron of the QEH during most of the time covered by this book. In this post she was a likeable figurehead and her nurses were not afraid of her. This was a cause for comment as Matrons of the day were usually seen as very authoritarian figures. With hindsight some of her ex-student nurses state that she was *"rather like Queen Elizabeth the Queen Mother, an educated intelligent and beautifully spoken lady"*. She was held by all in great respect, being a distinguished stylish lady who produced a well ordered serene hospital, managing it and its staff admirably. It was a polite place, and student nurses received a good 'modern' training. Her Deputy and Assistant Matrons did twice daily ward rounds and most had other responsibilities, for example Miss E. Collett was responsible for the domestic staff, and Miss M.Griffiths for the linen and laundry supplies and their staff.

Miss McKinnon retired as Deputy Matron 1950, her place was taken by Miss M. Ker-Ramsey a very strict nurse who had trained at St. Bartholomew's hospital, London. Her wonderful but tough methods streamlined much of the Nursing Administration department, but Sisters, staff nurses and student nurses *"quaked"* when she came to their wards to do a round as her powers of observation were well developed *"everything was noticed and all had to be in order"*. She seemed to delight in challenging her escorts on these rounds, with trick questions! Miss Barbara Scott was the QEH's third Matron, arriving in November 1955 and leaving in January 1962. (see Chapter 7)

The ward sisters

Overall, it seemed from the people interviewed that there were different types of sisters, one was *"caring, helpful, encouraging and promoted learning"*, another type, although managing a ward well was seen as *"powerful, gave minimal teaching, terrorised student nurses who were allocated there resulting in a negative experience"*. According to the people interviewed some sisters *"did appear to have a vocation, but were lazy"* other sisters *"saw their work as a job, worked hard on duty and enjoyed their off duty"*. Other commentators regarded the sisters as *"career people, who shouldered huge responsibilities, coped with lots of administrative chores, gave nursing care, guided and taught student nurses, talked to patients and relatives"*. Unfortunately the odd sister regarded *"visitors as intruders"*, others were *"very good at coping with relatives especially the bereaved"*.

Overall however, the nurses recall that the QEH Sisters imposed a *'quiet discipline'*, giving some praise, frightening their nurses sometimes and often reprimanding student nurses! Many individuals were remembered, Sister Megan Jones was *"approachable and managed her medical ward wonderfully"*. A few were remembered as *"obviously outstanding teachers"* others showed juniors *"the art of giving good skilled nursing care and the importance of accuracy"*, and another *"had a lovely touch with patients and student nurses"*. There were many very positive memories of the senior nurses. West 1 had a *"delightful"* Sister Cullen who was not strict but imparted a lot of knowledge to students. She was followed by young Sister Clarke. Sister Cliffe on West 2 seemed to be a *"stickler"* and under her regime one of the people interviewed confessed to having to clean and re-clean the same lockers three times. She seemed obsessed with the need to count instruments, cutlery etc. and student nurses had to cut a precise number of slices from a loaf of bread. Sister Churton was a new appointment on ward East Ground B and ran a well organised busy medical ward where student nurses felt explanations contributed to a high level of learning. Sister Timmington on West Ground, was seen as *"old type sister"* and *"unorthodox"* in her approach but she was always supportive of her nurses, teaching them well. She was much admired, always reacting quickly and efficiently in emergency situations although for some reason her nurses had to pretend that there were five dressing trolleys, when in fact only three existed. Sister Waldie of East 2B is recalled as a little bustling character who was seen as *"rather frightening"*.

Some ward sisters were recalled vividly for less positive reasons! For instance it was stated that *"ex-army Sisters were strict dragons"*, other were seen as *'tartars'*, another who *"seemed to delight in giving very hot dinner plates from the meal trolley to unsuspecting nurses"*, It seems that many felt that on most wards, sister seem to ensure that their nurses never sat down during their shift and even the hand-over report at the change of shits was received standing up!

Memories of some other personalities during the late 1950's surfaced. Sister E. Hamilton made Ward North 3B *"a happy ward"*; Sister L. S. Davis ensured

Ward East 5B was *"a contented and friendly place"*. Sister Hyland on East Ophthalmic *"set very high standards and was a good teacher"*. Ward East 3A was a good allocation as it provided *"a wealth of experience"*. One reporter remembered a strict Sister D. Bayliss giving very junior student nurses *"short days off"* on Ward East 1A, these must not have helped the continual tiredness which nurses would have experienced. Ward East Ground A run by Sister P. Tatlow (with Professor M. Arnott and Dr. J. Bishop as medical staff) was *"a busy and good medical ward"*. Miss Megan Jones was initially an Assistant Matron, later promoted to Deputy Matron; she was *"rather feared"*.

The medical staff
The medical consultants continued to be seen as important people and to some extent held in *"great awe"*. When they did their ward rounds (probably only twice weekly) nurses had ensure the patients were ready, by tidying their beds and lockers. The consultants came with their Registrar, House Officer and a group of medical students. In those days, they talked across the patients bed, rarely directly to the patient, and were *"economical with the truth"*. If the prognosis was poor, this deceit put great strains on the relatives and nurses, but this was then the 'norm'.

The consultants recalled by this group of nurses in the immediate post war period included Professors Stammers, Arnott, Brodie Hughes, Cloake, McLaren, along with Dr. Brian Taylor, Mr. d'Abreu and Mr. Scott Mason. Whilst in the late 1940's many new QEH consultant appointments including Dr. (Later Professor) George Whitfield *"charming, and polite to all"* Mr. Jack Leigh Collis, Mr. Arnold Gourevitch, a *"lively surgeon"* Dr. Owen Williams and Mr. Jack Small a *"showman, rather restless and noisy when in theatre"*. Two surgeons, Mr. A. d'Abreu and Mr. B. Brooke, were mentioned as being "special" as they held doors open for everyone *"even student nurses"*!

There were memories of being involved with the early development of good ileostomy bags and reporting results to Dr. C. Hawkins, Professor Hardy and Mr. B. Brooke who were also pioneering radical new surgery for patients with ulcerative colitis. Dr. W. Woodward was admired as an excellent anaesthetist, Professor Brodie Hughes was *"intimidating"* to many in his speciality of neuro surgery.

Once on the wards and wearing their yellow dresses and aprons, the short organdie cap, with fawn lisle stockings (later nylons which were available from about 1950), and Manfield, later Joyce, lace-up brown shoes, the student nurses led very busy lives. As noted in earlier Chapters the QEH nurses' uniforms were very modern when introduced in 1930's and continued to be well liked for many years after they were designed. The yellow dress *"protected and shielded"* the junior nurses by indicating their junior grade. Most of the people interviewed noted that once they wore their blue dresses became confident and enjoyed every shift whereas previously, for some, it was *"survival on a daily basis"* in the busy frightening life on the wards.

Qualifying as a Registered Nurse

Nurses remembered beginning to really to enjoy life on day and night duty, and in Study Block; particularly about the time of achieving Preliminary State Examinations. In the third year, Hospital Final Examinations were taken, these were considered harder than the Final State Examination for State Registration, which followed. The results of this last examination arrived from London, and as it was rare to have failures, the whole group could celebrate. The long cap was then worn with pride and joy and these nurses were now *"treated with respect"*. Becoming State Registered was a great relief, wearing the long cap was not only flattering and elegant but also the *"icing on the cake"*, with many new responsibilities lying ahead. This group were commonly referred to as 'the long cap blues' to distinguish them from the 'short cap blues', the pre registration student nurses.

In the last months of the World War, East 2B was still a military ward, full of wounded officers. The Final State Examination results had been published that day and one of the patients' favourite night nurse became a State Registered Nurse and received her long cap. Collectively the main ward patients asked the evening junior 'yellow nurse' to provide each of them with two sheets of Government issue toilet paper. In those days of great shortage a toilet roll was like gold, so she hesitated but they were very insistent and at about 8.50 p.m. their wishes were granted. The nurse turned as she left the ward and saw each patient fixing the two sheets to the back of their hair! After report a few minutes later the new 'long cap blue nurse' entered the ward to loud cheers from her 'long cap colleagues'. It was a very enjoyable episode.

There were, however, daunting new and increased responsibilities for the new 'long cap' nurse, both as ward administrators and in giving patient care. In addition they needed to consider teaching student nurses and taking care of relatives. From this perspective it was agreed that the fourth training year was excellent and gave the opportunity of learning to cope with all the extra responsibilities. Junior staff nurses had some choice about the ward or department in which they would spend this fourth year.

Living in the nurse home

As noted in previous Chapters, Nuffield House (the nurses home) bedrooms were intended for single occupancy but during the war, they had to be fitted with bunk beds. So student nurses left Southfield (the Preliminary Training School with accommodation) where 3–8 students had shared bedrooms for Nuffield House where two had to share rooms. This sharing lasted for about another 2 years, giving a lot of scope for mid-night feasts and much socialising but also providing wonderful support and lasting friendships. Junior student nurses had rooms on the sixth floor, but with the passage of months and years they were gradually allocated rooms on lower floors. The big front doors of Nuffield House were closed at 10 p.m. but the tunnel that connected it with the hospital was open until 11 p.m. If a nurse was planning to be out later, then she had to get a late pass from an Assistant Matron, with the inevitable questioning, and only one was permitted weekly. The lifts in Nuffield House were turned off at 11 p.m., so many stairs had to be climbed when coming in late.

As noted in Chapter 2, in 1946 the Annexe was built to provide extra accommodation for nurses. It was a single storey building, with several wings of individual bedrooms. The 19th PTS were the first occupants. Early on there were 'Peeping Tom' problems and worried student nurses visited the Deputy Matron to be informed that the solution was – 'A quick growing hedge of holly' The planting of a holly hedge was noted and tiny fragments exist even in the 1990's, and it was still only about a metre high – not a very good deterrent! Gradually the name 'Warren' was given to this much loved residence, where parties, access, independence and privacy reigned. If one had a room in the Annexe, which was on the ground floor illicit nocturnal access was much easier. The Principal Tutor, Miss Parnell, wryly commented on below knee bruises! Student nurses had bad days on duty when nothing went right, it was then that friends and on occasions the lady who cleaned their bedrooms came to their rescue with much chat over cups of tea.

In the 1950's the Annexe was extended; some greatly valued the single rooms and extra freedom there, but others considered the rooms and facilities awful. There was a wonderful camaraderie amongst student nurses in the home. However, whilst some found the nurses home a lovely comfortable place, where on bad days, *"one could always find a friend to whom to talk and soothe away the hurt"*, others found the unwritten rules and regulations childish and irksome especially as on the wards they had huge responsibilities.

Guest rooms were available close by the front door but rules were maintained. For example, male visitors were not allowed to stray from the ground floor. The various sitting rooms and the huge reception room (the Rec.) were grand and beautiful rooms, with well polished teak floors and still quite new comfortable chairs and occasional tables. Sisters and the senior staff nurses had their own sitting rooms, the former at the east end, the latter at the west end of Nuffield House; tea was brought to these rooms and much appreciated.

Nurses enjoy off duty at the Tennis Courts by Nuffield House.

It seems that by the Autumn of 1953, it was permissible for blue long caps (4th. year student nurses) who were of course over 21 years old, the age of majority, to become non-resident, quite a major step for the independence of nurses! By 1956 non-residency for student nurses was becoming more popular and it was permitted from the end of the first year; but only a minority became non-resident, perhaps due to the low salaries. Most stayed living in Nuffield House or in the Annexe.

In the late 1950's a dreadful murder occurred in Edgbaston, and there was great police anxiety for the safety of QEH nurses, as incriminating fingerprints had been found on the Annexe windows. To give protection, police patrolled the inside and outside of the hospital complex, particularly in the nurses' homes, throughout the day and night. Ex-night duty student nurses still recall their reassuring presence, but one very mature ward sister was *"not amused when going to the toilet in the middle of the night to find a young policeman in her path!"*

Social Life

Nurses entertained themselves by visiting the Oak Cinema in Selly Oak, attending concerts and film shows in the Rec. and with active pursuits such as

Off-duty friendship, nurses relaxing in Nuffield

playing tennis in the much used tennis courts, and mixed hockey.

As noted in earlier chapters a number of formal events were held in Nuffield House. Scattered throughout the year, for example, there were about 6 elegant formal Balls with dancing on the wonderful floor of the Rec. The ladies wore beautiful long gowns and long gloves and their partners had dinner jackets and often bought their ladies flowers. On entry to the ballroom, all guests were formally received by Matron and her party. Those nurses not attending the Ball sat on the stairs and peeped at the lovely dresses, enjoying the music of the dance band.

At a less formal level trips were made to the University Union 'hops' and during each study block, student nurses organised a well attended 'hop' in Nuffield House with soft drinks and perhaps a few 'eats'. This arrangement ensured a hop every 4–6 weeks! In the late 1940's tickets were 1/- (5p) which, given the salary levels, supported a hop every 4–6 weeks. Other small groups of friends with their boyfriends used to gather in the Library and have a private mini-hop dancing to records played on a wind-up gramophone. In bedrooms all over Nuffield House and the Annexe, social life was enacted by small groups of friends drinking tea and talking.

On pay days, friends treated themselves to tea at Kunzles which were tea shops at Five Ways and in the city centre. There were occasional coach trips to the theatre at Stratford- upon-Avon and all seats were quickly reserved; a packed supper was provided. Another interesting point was that in a tiny village, Rowney Green in Worcestershire, there was a hospital owned house. Nurses could book accommodation and arrange to spend their days or nights off there, they took their rations and a lady there cooked meals for them, whilst they rested and enjoyed themselves.

Post War Catering

Student nurses in the post war period vividly recalled the jam jars in which rations of butter, sugar and jam or marmalade was stored each week. Sadly the butter often went rancid before the end of the week! The rations of butter, sugar, jam were carried by all in string bags until the day in July 1954 when rationing was lifted.

During the post war years rationing continued and bread became rationed in July 1949, having not been rationed earlier. The milk allowance became more stringent in September 1949, being reduced to only 2 pints per person per week. Thankfully 1950 saw the end of petrol rationing in May and soap restrictions in September. So it was that these years saw the gradual return to peacetime conditions, but severe shortages persisted of almost every commodity. Student nurses had to learn to be very thrifty and frugal with all the stores and supplies which came to the wards. Sisters kept their stocks in locked cupboards, some hoarded unnecessarily, but years of deprivation had imprinted such habits.

Despite rationing, in the 1950's no one went hungry, but the food was dull and some reported that it was unsuitable and appalling for hard working student nurses. The catering department however, coped well with huge food difficulties. Despite the limitations a much appreciated lovely Sunday dinner was served. Some recalled with distaste 'steaks' of whale meat and eating unauthorised items behind the ward pantry door.

The nurses' dining room was a rather formal place, the tables laid with good quality cutlery and condiments and green place mats. Hierarchical systems still existed. Sisters used the right hand staircase down to their dining room whilst nurses used the left hand staircase to their much larger dining room. Once there they sat in groups according to seniority. On days off a friend could, during their

9 a.m. break bring breakfast upstairs to the bedroom of their off duty friend indicating a 'softening' of the rules.

Hospital developments
The war had a major impact on projected developments but the post war period saw some plans evolving. Until this time, the third floor of the administrative block was unfinished and just as the builders had left it a decade before. Now it was transformed, equipped and staffed, becoming two new wards (North 3A and 3B) specifically for the care of patients with malignant disorders. Some received their radiotherapy in the Deep X-ray department, others in the Beam Room, whilst radium needle implants were given to other patients. The consultants included Dr. Bromley and Mr. Bill Bond.

Hospital maintenance
The QEH wards were thoroughly cleaned annually and at least one or two wards were painted. To do this mammoth task efficiently, either East 3A or East 3B closed to private patients for about six months yearly to act as reception ward. Every week it received patients and staff from their own ward. If their ward was being cleaned, they stayed for 5 days and 4 nights, if it was to be painted they stayed for 3–4 weeks.

Christmas in Hospital
Christmas was a very special time at QEH throughout all the years covered in this book. In the weeks before, student nurses were much involved in preparing decorations for the ward. Each ward had its own Christmas tree with lots of fairy lights. These were displayed on Christmas Eve and removed three days later. During these few days, nurses toured the hospital wards to applaud or criticise other decorations.

Christmas Eve was very special and, following many rehearsals, on that evening a procession of nurses in uniform and cloaks carried lighted lanterns, visited every ward, singing a carol in each, in semi-darkness, afterwards they went to Sick Bay singing a carol there before returning to the Front Hall of Nuffield House where they gathered around the huge Christmas tree to sing 'Silent Night'. A number of nurses remembered Mr. Horne from the registration department taking on the role as musical director for many years. This yearly ceremony was a moving and wonderful recollection and made a huge impact on participants, patients, ward nursing and medical staff as well as off duty nurses in Nuffield House. Even later on Christmas Eve, over a hundred nurses in uniform walked to St. Peters' Church Harborne for Midnight Service.

Christmas Day – late night fancy dress parade.

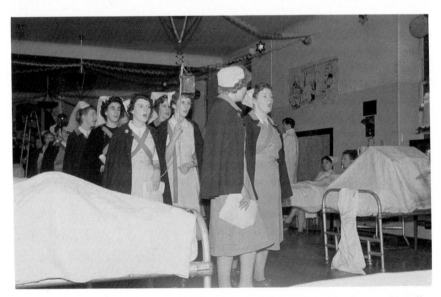

*Christmas carols – an annual event on Christmas Eve when hospital staff
toured the wards singing carols.*

A QEH Christmas greeting post-card – early 1950's.

On the two festive days, the day duty nurses worked a complete early and late shifts, doing minimal chores but giving proper nursing care. They had a coffee break in a room on the ward, often a 2 or 4 bedded ward, which had been made available for the nursing and medical staff as a recreation area for the Christmas period, in which to eat, drink and relax. On Christmas morning the consultants and their families visited their patients, and the Lord Mayor of Birmingham toured the wards. Relatives and friends came to visit their loved ones in large numbers on these two special days, and were included at teatime, quite a break from the routine in which little was available by way of refreshments for visitors to the hospital. In addition, Father Christmas came to every ward and had a present for each patient and usually the nurses too! A tradition developed in which most ward sisters prepared lovely suppers for their nurses on the two holiday days.

Much later on Christmas Day nurses and resident doctors went either individually or in ward groups to the impromptu Fancy Dress party held in Nuffield House Rec. It was a hugely entertaining and perfect end to a long day which was much enjoyed. The fancy dress was judged by the Matron, Miss Smaldon. Few went as individuals, most attending as ward team; someone recalled going as a group of Africans, another as green bottles. One year staff

Nurses Christmas pantomime performed annually in Nuffield House Rec –
(circa 1950's).
Photographs provided by Deborah Moriaty (56th PTS)

from the west block of the hospital went as a daisy chain which must have demanded a little co-ordination and planning!

In the days that followed there were the four Christmas dinners for student nurses, staff nurses, sisters and resident medical staff, being wonderfully arranged by Miss Richards. After each of these magnificent dinners, there was a performance in the Rec. of either the Nurses' Christmas Pantomime or the Residents Show. These productions had been long rehearsed, in secrecy to prevent stealing of each others' lines and dances and involved much work and fun. Being part of the pantomimes was an unforgettable experience The costumes were also specially made by the nurses 'using gorgeous material' and remembered as works of art. Others did back stage work under the direction of Freddie Brown (a Stores Officer) as the Stage Manager. A nurse who classed herself as a 'former Principal Boy' for three consecutive years recalled the superb efforts of the producer Sister Peggy Osmond, who also rewrote librettos for the main singers and chorus. (Sister Osmond continued to work at the QE until her retirement.)

The Matrons' Ball in January was a gift from Matron to her nurses, a superb, formal occasion, that finally brought the Christmas festivities to an end.

The Advent of the National Health Service

These five years (1946–50) were very important ones in all of the Hospitals and community services in Great Britain, including QEH. Discussions were taking place and decisions being made locally and nationally about the coming National Health Service. This change would mean the end of all voluntary and local authority hospitals.

During the dark days of World War Two, the very important Beveridge Report was published (in 1942). This became the origin of much post-war social legislation. The concept of free health care for all took some time to be accepted by doctors, as they feared civil servants status. The Act was passed at the end of 1946, but it was not implemented until July 1948. Within this framework, the QEH continued as a teaching hospital (being associated with the Medical Faculty of the University of Birmingham, and greatly involved in medical student education) and all such hospitals were given special self-governing rights. It was early in 1948 that the Minister of Health (Aneurin Bevan) visited QEH and although politely received by the majority, it is reported that an unknown minority were offensive, pouring red paint from a window!

On July 5th. 1948 the National Health Service was finally born. Until that date, QEH had been part of the "Birmingham United Hospitals" group, this was renamed the "United Birmingham Hospitals". To celebrate this remarkable change in Britain's' health system, QEH held a big tea party in the Rec. to which many important people were invited.

The 'short cap nurses' the first to third year students, were not invited so none were present, but one 'long cap blue' (a 4th year, junior staff nurse) was there as were several ward sisters. Matron took this junior staff nurse to meet a lady who tugged at her uniform and asked " *Do you like it?*" Thankfully she replied in the affirmative as it appeared the lady was Miss Bowes (now Mrs Whitehurst), who had been the first Matron of the QEH and, with Norman Hartnell, had been responsible for the design of the QEH nurses' uniforms! (See Chapter 2)

Life as a student nurse in the early National Health Service years seemed very little different, For the patients this meant free consultations and treatment from the family doctor and hospital doctors, dentists and opticians. This was important as from its the outset the QEH was a voluntary hospital. As such, Lady Almoners collected money from those patients who could afford to pay in part or in full for their care and treatment. This system ceased for the military patients and must have restarted after the end of the war, but it was not recalled by the people interviewed in this project. However the legacy of this collecting work meant the nurses remembered the Almoners were not always welcome to the patients who tended to view them suspiciously until the advent of the NHS when they became known as Medical Social Workers and gradually their image altered in the eyes of the patients.

Obviously the months between mid 1948 and the end of 1950 were spent adjusting to very new funding arrangements and different governing structures. These major changes seemed not to greatly impinge on the QEH student nurses except for the most welcome doubling of the ' training allowance'. First year nurses monthly pay packets now contained about £8. Salaries in the early 1950's are indicated in Figure 5.1. In addition their training allowances, and all other nursing salaries, now included a deduction to the NHS Superannuation scheme and National Insurance contributions. Previously student nurses had not contributed to a superannuation scheme, although qualified nurses belonged to the Federated Scheme.

The Coronation

Another major event in the life of the hospital was the coronation in 1953. Nurses remember this as being '*very like Christmas*' in that the normal routines of the day were changed and great efforts made to enable patients and staff to watch the coronation. Television sets were bought in for each ward area and a big television screen was installed in one of the rooms in Nuffield House and remained there after the event.

Figure 5.1
Yearly salaries for student nurses 1950–54

1950/1 1st year student nurses £210	)	£100 deducted for emoluments.
1951/2 2nd year student nurses £225	)	Other deductions were made for National
1952/3 3rd year student nurses £235	)	Insurance and Superannuation
1953/4 4th year student nurses £240	)	contributions.

The QEHNTS marked the occasion with the special edition of the Nurse training booklet with a glorious coloured front cover depicting Her Majesty and a special commemorative tin of toffees was given to each nurse. An account of working on a QEH ward on coronation day can be found in the next Chapter.

The late 1950's
These last years covered by this book saw the conclusion of QEHNTS. The house known Southfield continued to be the home and school for the new QEH student nurses for their first few months. By the 1950's just a half day a week was spent on the hospital wards, with nurses wearing unflattering green gowns. The rest of the week was spent learning the theory and practice of nursing and associated subjects in the school premises at Southfield. Miss V. C. Whiter was the Principal Tutor, and was greatly respected, always kind she "*never terrorised*" the learners. Miss Jean Waldie (a QEH trainee herself who became a tutor about 1955) was a "*formidable petite tutor*", who constantly urged individuals to do better.

As with previous generations once on the wards these inexperienced young student nurses had to adapt quickly to a very new life. Although the shift system remained 'special' as most hospitals still operated a split shift system of off duty, it was accepted that shift work was stressful (7 a.m. to 4.30 p.m. or 3.30 p.m. to 11 p.m. – this later changed to 10 p.m.). Some did remember a certain relaxing of the rules in terms of controlling private lives. For example, initially there was no method of asking for a particular time off duty, but later a request system operated. This meant the for the first time student nurses who wished to make plans for some special event could try and ensure they had the day off as necessary. It should be noted however, that asking did not always mean receiving!

The student nurses allocated for training at the General Hospital were now well established in Priorsfield next door, and the new Central training school

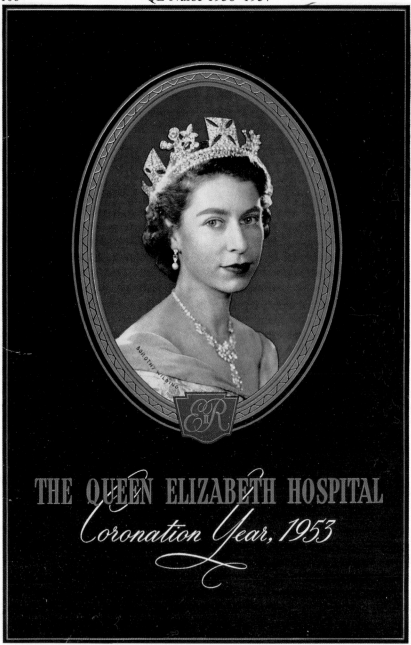

Front cover, Coronation Anniversary book

was emerging (see Chapter 3). As a result there was much more sharing between students of both hospitals with on and off duty activities. One commentator recalled a joint lively party, where they *"drank Baby Cham and did a conga all round the huge gardens"*.

The first group under the unified Queen Elizabeth School of Nursing (QESN) commenced training on 8th October 1957. They were allocated the Group number 201. The rational for this is unclear although it is known that the GHB had got to PTS number 165, the QEHNTS had got to PTS 68 so perhaps to take the group number forward seemed less confusing at the time. It is interesting to note that in the last five years of the QEHNTS some 585 QEH student nurses gained their State Registered Nurse qualification. However, the result of the transition to the new central training school meant the last 120 students did not receive the greatly prized QEHNTS badge described in Chapter 3. Instead they were awarded the new badge designed for the QESN trainees. Nurses remembered this causing individual hurt and discontent as they had entered their training anticipated the award of the unique QEH badge and their vision was not attained as a result of the organisational changes of the Schools.

Conclusion

Overall, the four years of nurse training at the QEH were seen as marvellous years in the opinion of almost all people interviewed in this project. The whole atmosphere of this huge well ordered hospital was one of serenity, politeness and high standards where student nurses received good experience and learning opportunities. The greatest blessing though for each and all of them was the wonderful friendships they made which continue to blossom and have lasted through many succeeding years.

Chapter 6

The Male Nurse Experience

In September 1946 thirty nine members of the 25th PTS arrived in Southfield, three of these were male nurses. This was a new development for the QEHNTS that had previously been dominated by females and it is thought to have been one of the first SRN training schools to include male nurses. They were however, treated differently from the outset, for example the men were always non resident where the pattern for the female student nurses was compulsory residency. Whilst possibly perceived as an advantage for the men this meant travel time was added to the long working days.

The table in the Appendices indicates the pattern of male nurses completing their training in the QEHNTS during the time span of this book. A high leaving rate amongst the men who joined the PTS listed can be seen. Sadly two of the first three male nurses left the first programme but Alfred Charles Stevens, qualified as a SRN with the 25th PTS in November 1949, later to become a tutor in the QESN.

At that time nurses were able to train for other parts of the professional register such as psychiatric nursing as direct entry student nurses, they were then encouraged to complete a course leading to SRN to give them an appropriate 'range' of qualification for their career in nursing. As these nurses already had achieved acceptable qualifications they were allowed to join the second year of the training programme. These students nurses, who entered QEHNTS almost monthly, were known as Group A students. From the Autumn of 1946 male students feature amongst this small numbers of second year, Group A student nurses. The first second year male student at the QEH was Mr. F. May followed a few months later by Mr Geoff Lanchbury who went on to become the first male charge nurse (the title given to men who worked at the same grade as ward sisters) at the QEH.

The role of the male nurse in a female dominated profession has been singled out to illustrate some of the 'differences' that may be observed in their experiences. There still remain only 2 men in the QE Nurses League and so note of their experience is needed for the male nurse of the present and future to relate to, as their careers develop.

In this account we have the benefits of ready access to the memories of Jeff Wood, one of the compilers of this text who was able to help 'bridge this gap'. This was seen as important for many of the men who trained and worked in the QEH undertook leadership roles in nursing in years to come. Indeed Jeff himself moved into nurse education and took a lead role in many initiatives in nursing education in his role as Director of Nursing Education at the South Birmingham School of Nursing.

Starting training
Jeff Wood remembers going to the Labour Exchange to discuss the possibility of training to be a nurse. At the exchange he was offered a choice of three training schools of which the QEH was one. He chose the QEH *"simply because he had been an out-patient in the hospital and so knew where it was!"*. He should have started with the 48 PTS in June 1952 but, as part of his army reserve requirement was required to go to annual camp, and he was, therefore, advised to start training in October. This was of course a major difference from the female students for they were not expected to fulfil army reserve duties.

Jeff acknowledged it was unusual for *"a chap to go straight into nursing"*. He came to this from a Grammar School education and held the equivalent of eight 'O Levels' when he left school at 16. In 1950 he was called up for the army, and completed two years service in the Royal Engineers. He admitted that this decision to start training resulted in being

"teased by my Black Country macho mates about being in a 'feminine' job but I do not think it really worried me as I could see a future in the job as it was at the time and I also enjoyed it very much"

To this day Jeff is not sure why he became a nurse. His grandmother had been a ward maid for 25 years at Wordsley Hospital near Stourbridge, and his mother who did all sorts of jobs, was at her happiest when working at hospital, in posts that would today be known as ward auxiliary or care assistant. Her last hospital job was a Matron's maid to the matron at Prestwod Sanatorium, Stourbridge.

The Preliminary Training School
At the time he started nursing Jeff was living in Quarry Bank, Staffordshire and used to cycle to QEH , a journey taking about one hour! He was the only male nurse in the 49 PTS and remembered arriving (on his bike) on a sunny October afternoon, and sitting at the back of the classroom at Southfield, and through the door came 43 females, all young, in fact –

"all younger than me as I was 22 by then. After the initial shock I never really felt strange being the only chap amongst so many females. I think,

*on reflection, I rationalised it by relating the structure of the hospital
to the structure of the army. There was a hierarchy and I fitted in at the
appropriate point. Additionally, I felt, the seniors, even the second
years, had knowledge and skills about what I was doing that I did not
have and so I just got on with the job"*

Overall he concluded that, in nursing, there were common problems and
experiences that he had found in the army. Occasionally, for example, there
were "overbearing superiors" perhaps only one or two sets above him and mostly
younger. He felt however, he could cope with this and was able to *"retaliate
very politely as you learn these things in the army!"*

The PTS was an enjoyable time for someone who had always enjoyed school.
Miss McLennan was the tutor in charge.

Ward experiences
Jeff felt prepared for his first ward experience as a half a day a week in PTS was
spent in the wards where the student nurses were going to work. One of the
things he remembered was seeing a lumbar puncture and, while it was a bit of a
shock to see a man with a needle in his back, *"the girls (fellow students) and he
took it in their stride"*.

His first ward was East Ground B, (EGB) managed in those days by Sister
Churton. The consultants largely treated male nurses as 'junior ranks' in the
army. The medical staff on the ward at the time included, Professor (later Sir)
Melville Arnott, a Resident Medical Officer (RMO) called Dr Butler and the
Reader was Dr K. W. Donald who later became the Professor of Medicine at
Edinburgh. Dr Bishop and Dr Wade, both professors later, were registrars at the
time, and the house doctor Dr Geoff Oates, later to become a consultant surgeon
– *"It was he who taught me the nurses role in putting up a drip"*. Geoff Oates
"treated one as a junior colleague, always ready to teach". Furthermore he
supported the social slide of life by *"selling me a Dinner Jacket for which I paid
£4 borrowed from my mother. The jacket, purchased in 1953 is in still in my
wardrobe and was last used in 1992!"*

Sister Churton's motto was 'a place for everything and everything in its place'
She was seen as being in advance of her time in many ways in that, for example,
she used a 'team nursing' approach in 1952. (Experienced nurses will note that
this approach to managing care was not widely adopted in England until the
1970's). Also, in 1952 Sister Churton , did what she called her 'social round' in
which she talked to patients about their families, their work and so on. At that
time not many ward nurses had thought of doing such things as the focus was
largely on the disease or medical problem.

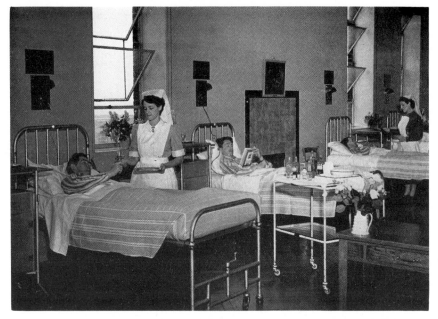

*One of the Main Wards. The largest wards in the Hospital contain
only 16 beds, and each is part of a unit of 30 complete with all necessary
auxiliary services.*

One of the memorable things Jeff remembered about EGB was that staff
could not go off the ward at the end of a span of duty until they had accounted
for all the teaspoons to make sure there were enough to go around for the
patients having boiled eggs for breakfast. It was however, a small issue and one
which the nurses could understand the rationale for the action, and overall,
the experience on EGB as seen as offering a *"first class experience and gave
me an excellent foundation of the nursing care in the rest of my experience
in nursing"*.

Practical experiences.
Overall the practical experience for the men was very similar to the female
student nurses except they did not go to the Women's Hospital but went instead
to the Special Clinic for Venereal Diseases at the General Hospital, Birmingham.
If there were too many nurses for night duty some only did six weeks and not
the standard twelve week block, and it was often the men who had the experience
reduced. In fact the men had two allocated experiences in the genito-urinary

departments, a useful training for night duty when the male nurses were commonly asked to undertake any male catheterisation procedures and male pelvic shaves. Paediatric experience was partly in the Outpatient Department at the Children's Hospital. where the superintendent at that time was an idiosyncratic Welsh lady called Sister Wynn-Jones. She was a "real character" who evolved a special duty roster for the men " *because you have to come in every day boy isn't it*"!

A later memory was of Coronation day in 1953. On that day Sister Tennant, then sister on E3B, the private ward, asked if we would like to "*have a normal day or get through the work, have coffee on the ward and then watch the coronation on the television*" which is what they did. A television set had been hired by the hospital management for each ward to enable all to watch the coronation. As a result Jeff remembered

> "*We did all the treatments and dressings by 10.30 a.m. Then we pushed all the patients out of the side wards into the main award – it was very crowded and we had to clamber over the beds to get bed pans or urinals delivered to patients – but they were all able to watch.*"

The kitchens put on a special dinner,

> "*almost Christmas dinner without the pudding as we had Turkey . . . We stayed on the wards for lunch on that day and had the scraps from the dinner trolley which was most unusual as strictly speaking we were not allowed to eat on the wards. Although we used to drink tea out of basin – don't ask why the basin but that is what we did! One of my little tricks on the late shift was to spread the minced chicken that had come up for the special diets on toast – although we had to be quick before the night sister came on her rounds or do it after she had gone!*"

Impact of senior nurses

Miss Smaldon, the Matron, was rarely seen on the wards by the juniors, although "*her ideas and personality permeated the hospital*". The day to day running of the hospital was undertaken by Miss Ker-Ramsey who was the deputy Matron, her presence was "*very obvious as she was a martinet and I think even the sisters were afraid of he*r". She would regularly do rounds with a student nurse which was again quite uncommon in those days . But, despite her apparent fierceness, she was very kind person and "*certainly I felt she was like the Brigadier coming round and that is how I related to her!*"

It was whilst on his first ward that Jeff met Dorothy who was then a staff nurse on EGB. "*We starting going out together and 18 months later were married*" (and still are today!). Jeff remembered:–

"When I wanted to get married I needed to seek permission from the Matron as this was one of the regulations in the nurses rules at the time. When I approached Miss Ker- Ramsey to ask for this permission she said 'you do not need to ask permission from me Mr Wood'. I said, 'It says in my contract Ma'am that I do, student nurses need permission from the Matron.' When she stopped laughing I told her that I wanted to marry Dorothy Davies. 'Ah yes', she said, 'she was one of ours, she was in the 35th PTS . . .'; just like that, She had a fantastic memory.'

The conditions of service referred to can be seen in Chapter 3 (Figure 3.2). In this context it is worth noting that when single, Jeff's salary had been about three pounds a week; on marrying he got an extra ten shillings!

Another memory of the senior nurses was of one of the assistant matrons who would come around with her cloak wrapped around her and say *"is there any blood left over from the operation nurse?"* If there was blood left over from the transfusion bottles, which was not unusual, she would produce a lemonade bottle into which she would tip the blood and she would use this to feed her tomatoes. The Assistant Matrons and some of the tutors had a small allotment plot on the west side of Nuffield house.

Ward sisters were very capable, and set high standards. One Sister admonished me once by saying *"this was not really the standard I expect of you"* and, as *"I held this sister in great esteem that served to make me try very hard not to fall below the expectations"*. All of this contributed to the learning experience.

"The ethos of QEH, as I realised later, was that it was not only an environment where people were cared for but it was a learning environment as there were students of so many different disciplines and I think the ethos of education permeated right through from professor to porter – I only realised this later when I worked in other hospitals where the 'work ethic', but not the learning ethic, was well established"

Memories of the medical staff

Amongst the consulting staff were Professor d'Abreu who was seen as a very gentle man. He told us in a lecture once that wound infection was *"caused by surgeons, not nurses, but please- dear ladies do not tell my colleagues as they would not like it!"* He also pioneered the minimal dressing – prior to that we used to put a lot of packing on wounds. Dr George Whitfield, well respected physician, later Professor, *"very charming – always called the men 'Dear boy', even when they were students!"* Professor Cloake the neurologist was very eminent but

*"one had to be really quiet during the ward round you could not really
enter the ward when his round was on unless you really had to. For
example, a nurse was doing a dressing one day in the days when we
had metal kidney dishes and bowls that had no lids. To cover them we
balanced another bowl on top of these and the nurse was going very
gently along the ward when she hit a little obstruction on the floor and
the bowls smashed to the floor and the noise was terrific. I heard
Professor Cloake say 'nurse why don't you turn the whole damned lot
upside down and be done with it"!*

The educational experience

The Sister Tutors were led by Miss Parnell, the Principal Tutor, who presented a
stern but fair approach. There was also Miss Snee who was very knowledgeable
*"you couldn't catch her out on anything to do with signs or symptoms of nursing
care".* There were no male tutors in those days but subsequently Mr. A. C.
Stevens was the first man appointed as a tutor. He was remembered by some as
demonstrating 'tutor potential' early in his career when faced with a patient
anxious about mild constipation. He advised the patient that he had worked
with an African tribe that only had their bowels open once a month and this was
considered usual, the patient relaxed and the problem resolved! Steve, as he was
widely known, was followed in due course by Mr. John McNamara who became
the next tutor. Mr. McNamara remembers watching the QEH being built, when
as a boy, he did his paper round in Edgbaston!

The examinations system has been discussed in Chapter 3. It should be noted
that there were some differences between male and female student nurse in the
examinations. Each group had to do a compulsory question but these were
directed at different topics for the male student.

Mention was made in Chapter 3 of the experience book that student nurses
had to get filled in to illustrate their practice experience prior to the final
practical examinations. There were some problems with encountering the range
of medical conditions, as the QEH was a very specialised hospital. There was
no orthopaedic surgeon so it was rare for student nurses to see a fractured femur.
In fact the list of diagnoses allocated to patients in the Medical ward, EGB read
rather like the chapter headings in a medical text book!

The male nurse group

Male nurses formed a very small part of the staff in the 1950's. In total there
were about 12 male nurses in a staff of 3–400 females. Most of the men were
previously registered in psychiatry or in mental handicap (known then as mental
sub-normality). A number of the early post war male students entered under a

special scheme for medical orderlies from the forces to undertake a twelve month training programme leading to registration as a nurse.

There were various attitudes to male nurses in the predominantly female nursing profession and Jeff Wood felt that many male nurses around the country had a "hard time". There were very evident differences even in QEH. For example, all the male nurses were called by their Christian names – this was very unusual as all the girls were called by their surname. Jeff Wood remembered the exception to this as the Sister who *'called us all nurse'*. He confessed this was the only time the title 'grated' on him as he had the 'little feeling' that the title 'nurse' used in this way was feminine. Later he acknowledged that although he recognised the female association with the word nurse he feels now it is a much more neutral word. Overall he

> *"never felt an anti male experience from the sisters although he did occasionally from the doctors, (probably house doctors, the most junior grade). Most of the registrars, and certainly a lot of the consultants, had had experience of male medical orderlies undertaking nursing duties during the war and were quite conversant when working with us."*

This was reflected in part by some characters in the medical ranks. For example one senior genito-urinary (GU) surgeon was seen to be something of a 'misogynist' who would say to me *'boy, come along, we will go the clinic'*. We went to the clinic with Geoff Lanchbury, the only man with the same rank as sister in the QEH, and Knox, (whose other name generations of nurses in the QEH GU unit did not know as he was always 'Knox'). He was in a post, that nowadays would be known as the theatre technician. Jeff remembers *"we three would join the surgeon in the cystoscopy clinic where his manner was entirely different"*.

Another indication of this surgeon's attitude came when Jeff was a third year student on the private ward and the surgeon came at about 6.30 p.m. to see a patient:-

> *"I said 'I'll get sister', to which he replied 'I don't want Sister boy-you'll do, take me to my patient, you know him don't you?'. 'Yes sir' 'then take me to him' 'I'll get Sister '– 'damn you boy I don't want Sister!'.*
>
> *When we got to the patient, Sister came in and I said 'I'm sorry Sister – I did not know you were here'; the surgeon said 'Go away Sister, I've got the boy that's all I need'. Exit one flustered Sister! When he finally left the ward I went to Sister and apologised and she was very good and said 'never mind I do understand'."*

Miss B. Scott (Matron) and senior nursing staff. Note the ratio of male to female staff.

Jeff concluded that, on balance, men in nursing were tolerated rather than accepted although that *"might be too harsh"*. He noted that

> *"I personally was always courteously treated by the nursing hierarchy and the ward sisters seemed to treat the men almost as they treated the girls although I think at the time there were a little afraid of us and used their rank in slightly different fashion, very difficult to describe. I suppose they were more authoritarian with the girls and expected them to do what they were told as of right whereas they used their authority to ask the men to do the various tasks."*

This was also borne out by a letter, dated 1996, from John E. Giles who felt he had been shown great courtesy throughout his QEH training. The letter, written when he was in his nineties, spoke of his gratitude for the training he had received. The ratio of male to female nurse is illustrated in the picture above of the group of sisters and Charge nurse taken at the end of the period covered by this book.

Staff Nurse Jeff Wood receiving Gold metal and other prizes (195*).

Conclusion

Out of the ranks of the male nurses at the QEH during this time a number went on to develop careers at senior levels in nursing throughout the country. However, in the early years of the QEH it was the female leaders that were remembered in the hospital as will be seen in the next chapter.

Chapter 7

The Nurse Leaders at QEH 1938–1957

All large organisations owe their existence and development to key people who are outstanding in their leadership qualities and the impact they have upon those working with them. In an institution, such as the QEH, the number of figures who could be identified under this category is large and it is recognised that, in acknowledging some, we may be criticised for omissions. Consequently, the focus will only be on a few leaders, largely the three women who had the role of Matron in the time span covered by this book. As noted throughout the book a number of other people emerged as 'characters' or leaders in nursing in the course of the interviews completed for this book. Clearly this does not form an exclusive list of those who played an important role in shaping nursing at the QEH and there is a lot more scope to cover the contribution made by those people but space does not permit here.

The influences of the staff from the Queen's Hospital leading to the developments of the QEH are discussed in Chapter 2 of this book. It should also be noted that the General Hospital played an important role. The General Hospital has a long standing history being the first hospital to be developed in Birmingham in the late 18th Century. As the major general hospital in the city it was inevitable that the staff from this hospital played a part in the development of the new Centre Hospital (later to become the QEH). This was evident in the appointment of the first matron of the new Centre Hospital, Miss Bowes, and the senior nurses who moved with her to the new hospital site.

Miss Gladys Marguerite Bowes A.R.R.C. 1893–1965

This North Country lady became the first matron of the new Centre Hospital having been appointed the Matron of the Birmingham Hospital Centre. Her work in nursing can be traced back to the 1914–18 war in which Miss Bowes served in a V.A.D. capacity on a hospital ship in the Mediterranean Sea, in Salonika and various military hospitals. It seems that she continued this role at Croydon Military Hospital, until, at the age of 27 years in 1920, she received a V.A.D. Scholarship and commenced a formal nurse training course at the Nightingale School of Nursing at St Thomas's Hospital, London. During this she contracted

Scarlet Fever and spent time as a patient in Stockwell Fever Hospital. She completed her training in 1924 and was awarded the Gold Medal indicating her prowess in both theory and practice of nursing.

Miss Bowes went on to achieve the Central Midwifery Board midwifery qualification whilst working at the Radcliffe Infirmary in Oxford, She then became a night sister for a year at the Royal Sussex Hospital. This was followed by a Red Cross Scholarship that allowed her to spend a year studying at Bedford College, London before returning to her alma mater as a Night Sister.

It appears that the subsequent two years were spent at the College of Nursing as an Acting Education Officer and doing more personal study; this led to the award of the University of London Diploma in Nursing with a distinction in hospital administration. In 1930 Miss Bowes was appointed as Matron of St. Andrews Hospital, Bow, London. A personal recollection of a St. Andrews probationer at that time (a mother of a QEH nurse) states

> "Miss Bowes was quite a character, doing the ward rounds accompanied by a small dog; she once caught me with a cooked 'left over' kipper in my pocket which I was eating as Matron arrived! On completion of her round Matron said 'Go now and enjoy your catch in the Kitchen!'"

In 1932 this austere, capable and highly respected lady became Matron of the General Hospital Birmingham, a post she held for 5 years. Her leadership and administrative abilities were recognised and appreciated by those responsible for the building and managing of the new Centre Hospital. So it was that Miss Bowes was appointed as Matron to this new and unique, hospital centre in 1937.

The months between the appointment and the opening of the hospital must have been very busy as she was one of the key people responsible for the commissioning tasks and all the major and minor decisions associated with a development of this kind. This included contributing towards the design of the novel nurses uniforms with Norman Hartnell (see Chapter 2). This was a lasting legacy as it was worn until 1973 when the uniform eventually changed to the more modern 'overall' we see today.

Other aspects of Miss Bowes history have been noted in earlier chapters. She managed the first couple of years of the new QEH through the early days of war. She then, quietly and unexpectedly married a bank manger and became Mrs Whitehurst. She acceded to the wishes of the Board of Governors staying in post until a new Matron was appointed. This was unusual for the times as married nurses did not work in hospitals at that time. Consequently she played an important role as described in Chapter 4, caring particularly for many of the Dunkirk wounded.

Miss Bowes is remembered for her business like and helpful manner which was balanced and supported by a sense of democracy. She made a point of eating one meal weekly with her nurses in the dining room. She was also remembered for walking around the hospital during air raid alerts wearing a tin hat and often accompanied by her red setter dog called Adolf! She finally left the QEH in August 1940 and the only other information available about her in this text refers to a little story associated with the launch the NHS described in Chapter 5 (QEHNL Magazine 1995).

Miss Catherine Smaldon CBE (1905–1980)

The appointment of this lady as Matron of QEH. was an inspired choice and her 15 years in this post from 1940 to 1955 proved the rightness of the decision. Little is known about Miss Smaldon until 1940. She had trained as a nurse in the mid twenties at Charing Cross Hospital and proudly wore its impressive badge. Following qualification as a SRN she held several posts culminating in the appointment of Matron of the Brompton Hospital. It was from this post, at the age of 35 years, she arrived at the QEH as the second Matron, succeeding Miss Bowes, in August 1940.

Whilst some of our interviewees remembered her as a diminutive lady, wearing a dark blue uniform dress and a large triangular cap (Matrons chose their own uniform) one of the most striking memories was her part in the decision in 1943/44 for Gaumont-British to make the film "The Student Nurse". Such an initiative was quite significant and ahead of its time and greatly enhanced recruitment, not only at QEH. but also nationally (see Chapter 3).

Miss Smaldon is given credit for a number of other innovative initiatives. For example in 1942–3 the 'Block system' of nurse training, described in Chapter 3 as possibly the first in the country, was a major development. She also addressed the problem of the long hours nurses worked and sought to rectify the situation in 1946/47 by introducing a proper shift system and banishing split shifts (i.e. shifts in which nurse worked several hours in the morning, had a couple of afternoon hours off and returned to work on the wards until late in the evening) Miss Smaldon announced this change at a huge staff meeting held in Nuffield House Recreation room (the Rec.) when she stated her wish for nurses to have all their on duty in one 8 hour span and all their off duty in another one. This innovative method of working was unique for many years, and even 10–12 years later nurses elsewhere were still crippled by awful split shifts. These were remarkable innovations of the day, and possibly unequalled in the country from many years as the ideas were 'ahead of their time'.

Miss Smaldon had a remarkably affable manner, entering into the off duty life of the hospital In the war years she initiated and became fully involved in a

Miss Smaldon with her CBE – pictured with Miss Ker-Ramsey outside Buckingham Palace.

Dramatic Society. During rehearsals members were called by their first names but away from the activities of the society they were referred to as 'Nurse . . .'. It is thought that the Christmas Fancy Dress Parade, described in Chapter 5, was almost certainly her creation. On one occasion three resident doctors went as Red Indians complete with wigwam made of Balkan frame poles and a counterpane; just by this they lit a fire on a piece of metal. Everyone was sure this trio would win the prize until Matron arrived wearing a swimsuit and carrying a towel!

Once the Americans were in the war (December 1941) some were stationed in a camp on the northern outskirts of Birmingham. It was their practice to inform Nuffield House about the dances and send a coach for nurses wishing to attend. Miss Smaldon and Sister Ailsa Bird always joined; being entertained by the Officers. In return there were dances in Nuffield House to which the Americans were invited. (At this time Sister Bird's husband was a prisoner of war in Japanese hands, although later released.)

Miss Smaldon was appointed in 1955 as Chief Nursing Officer and Principal of the QESN (Chapter 2). This unusual title and position was granted ten years before the Salmon report led to its more common usage. She ensured the amalgamation of the three United Birmingham Hospitals Nurse Training Schools into one fledgling School of Nursing named by George VI after his consort, Queen Elizabeth, and confirmed at a Board of Governors meeting in February 1950 at which a letter was read from the Home Office making this announcement.

Her outstanding contribution to nursing was recognised when she was elected to the General Nursing Council for England and Wales and later was its Chairman and it was for this work she was awarded the CBE. The Insignia and Citation were donated to the QEHNL after her death.

Before her retirement in 1964 Miss Smaldon left Birmingham for Herefordshire and later moved to Devon, where she died in 1980. Miss Smaldon left a legacy as being a 'wonderful leader and a delightful lady and, as can be seen in earlier Chapters, held in great esteem by nurses in the QEH and eventually by nurses nationally for her role and work with the General Nursing Council.

Another important factor that should be noted was that in 1944 Miss Smaldon founded the QEHNL and was the first President of this group. So, in an indirect way, the origins of this book need to be credited to her.

Miss B.B. Scott

Miss Scott was appointed Matron to succeed Miss Smaldon, when the latter became Chief Nursing Officer to the United Birmingham Hospitals.

The new Matron was born and brought up in the West Country and trained as a nurse at London's Middlesex Hospital prior to the 1939–1945 war. After qualifying as a SRN, then as a midwife, Miss Scott gained certificates in tropical nursing and industrial nursing. Having planned her career carefully she held a series of posts in her training school – as a staff nurse, a ward sister and theatre sister and for four years as night superintendent. Before her appointment to the QEH, posts as assistant and deputy matrons were important administrative experiences.

Miss Scott came to the QEH when the traumas and shortages of war were healing, the National Health Service was fully established, nursing and nurse education were beginning to experience the first faint stirrings of change. She came from a traditionalist nursing background to a milieu that was possibly more progressive than that with which she was familiar. As Matron, Miss Scott had her office was in the same building as her highly respected predecessor and this cannot have been easy, but there was no doubt amongst her nurses that Miss Scott was in charge of QEH.

This tall commanding lady whose height was enhanced by a high lacy cap, wore a blue uniform, the personal choice allowed to Matron. She was often seen doing *"very formal and testing ward rounds"*. her decorum and protocol extended to Matron's flat in Nuffield House and she was probably the last Matron to live there in a life style that was considered 'correct and appropriate' for one in her position.

After just over 5 years Miss Scott left the QEH to become Matron of Selly Oak Hospital, Birmingham, in January 1962. She left a continuing impression of probably the last of the 'old style' Matrons.

Miss B. Scott (Matron) and Mr B. Sylvester (House governor) and the ladies of the Linen League, inspecting gifts for patients in QEH at Christmas time.

Other leaders
Other nurse leaders played a part in the evolution of the nursing at QEH during the time span covered by this book.

From an educational viewpoint **Miss E. Woodhouse (1945–1981)** was important as she was the first Principal Tutor to the new QEHNTS. She trained at the General Hospital, Birmingham, completing her SRN course in about 1926. She subsequently qualified as a Sister Tutor, worked as a tutor at the General Hospital and was then recruited by Miss Bowes to become the Principal Tutor to her brand new training school which began with the 1st. PTS on 4th October 1938.

Miss Woodhouse, affectionately known as 'Toots', was seen as a strict but fair Sister Tutor who laid down important nursing principles, insisting on high standards. She left QEHNTS in Spring 1945 and died in 1981.

Miss Megan Jones began working at the QEH in March 1939. She was a Staff Nurse on E2B with Sister B. Byrne; a quick move followed and when war was declared in September 1939, she found herself, along with other nurses, sitting 'somewhere on East Ground' knitting balaclava helmets and waiting for casualties. The hospital and the war did not keep these nurses waiting long, and Staff Nurse Jones move to E1B. Miss Jones was appointed Sister of E1B in June 1940 with **May Spencer** Sister on E1A, and with **Sister Turpin** the Senior Sister over both wards. Sister Turpin later moved to ward East 3. In 1957 Miss Jones took the Housekeeping Course and became an Assistant Matron. She looks back on the time with 'horror', as her responsibilities were the laundry and linen services – not much joy or reward after the responsibilities and interest of a heavy medical ward. Despite this Miss Jones remained in the sphere of nursing administration at QEH until her retirement in 1974.

Miss Mary Ellen Griffiths (1908–1984) was born in Barry, South Wales, her parents having moved there when the Docks opened in 1884, she was one of eight children.

Her maternal grandmother, Ellen Jenkins, was a hill farmer's wife and a very skilled, (though of course unqualified) midwife. Her paternal grandmother, Mary Griffiths, was a sister of the Reverend Wynford Rees, whose son, General Wynford Rees, was a famous general in the Burma campaign, "Dagger Rees". Like Miss Griffiths, he too was short in stature, but gigantic in performance.

Miss Griffiths did her SRN and SCM training at Warneford General Hospital, qualifying in 1930 and 1932 respectively. On completion, she held both staff nurse and ward sister posts there and later returned to her training school to do the Housekeeping course. Sometime later, she became a night sister at Chesterfield Royal Infirmary.

Matron with senior nursing staff. Left to right: Miss E. Collett (House Sister),
Miss C. A. Smaldon (Matron), Miss M. Griffiths (Assistant Matron),
Miss E. Woodhouse (Principal Tutor).

In April 1938, she applied to Miss G. M. Bowes, Matron of The Centre
Hospital. Miss Griffiths was interviewed and accepted during that summer, her
rail fare being 'refunded with a postal order for 11/3d'. Her appointment was
delayed because of the threats of war. Matron of Chesterfield Royal Infirmary
had the majority of her State Registered Nurses in the Territorials and if war
was declared, they would disappear immediately, therefore she wished to retain
Miss Griffiths. However, with the Munich settlement in the later summer, the
two Matrons finalised arrangements for Miss Griffiths to leave Chesterfield for
Birmingham.

In October 1938, she took up her post in QEH as 'night superintendent
with an annual salary of £120 and uniform'. It is not known how long Miss
Griffiths held the post of night superintendent, but sometime in the early
1940's she became an Assistant Matron, holding this post until 1966, when the
Salmon system of nursing management was adopted by the QEH, and Miss
Griffiths became a Nursing Officer, and in 1969 was promoted to be a Senior
Nursing Officer. She retired at the very end of 1970, after over 32 years (well
over half of her life) at the QEH, the following comments were made in letters
to her.

"You leave this hospital, as you have always been, a person who is loved by all".

She continued to regularly attend QEHNL days, enjoying meeting those she knew and remembered so well, always showing and receiving much affection. She came too, to feel the bricks and corridors etc. of the actual building of the QEH, to which she was so attached and fond.

Miss Elizabeth COLLETT (1902–1982) was seen as an *"imposing and rather austere lady"* and came to the Centre Hospital as Nuffield House's first Home Sister from the Queen's Hospital where she had done her training in the 1920's and latterly been the Night Superintendent there. She arrived in Nuffield House about two weeks before the 1st PTS arrived on October 4th. 1938 and must have had a hectic time in those early months and years. Nuffield House was very much her domain for about 8–10 years and her presence there was acknowledged and on occasions feared by many student nurses. But beneath it all Miss Collett was a kind lady.

In the late 1940's she moved from Nuffield House to be an Assistant Matron in QEH, there she was involved in twice daily ward rounds; her additional responsibility was for the hospital's domestic staff; she knew them well and they respected her.

Some years before retiring in 1962, she and Miss E. Richards (Catering Officer) 'went to live out' in the lodge to Southfield. In this they were pioneers, Miss Collett being the first Assistant Matron to become non-resident. Later she and Miss Richards moved to Worcestershire.

Miss Beatrice Byrne was an experienced General Hospital trained nurse who moved from the General Hospital to the QEH; initially as Ward Sister on ward E2B. Later she was the Night Superintendent for many years before becoming Nuffield House's last Home Sister and then later Sister of Sick Bay. Nurses in the late 1940's and early 1950's remember Miss B. Byrne being in charge. She created comfortable, safe surroundings and ensured that her patients received superb care. She was a very capable, observant and competent senior Sister and an excellent administrator, but was rather frightening for young student nurses. She retired in the late 1950's and died in 1992. Beatrice's sister **Miss Molly Byrne** also trained at the General Hospital, and she came to the new QEH in 1939 to be its first Theatre Superintendent, a post held for some nine years. She was another who demanded high standards and was *"rather feared"*. Molly died in 1991.

Miss Marjorie BOMFORD (1912–1988), who was seen as a *"delightful capable lady"*, came to QEH as Principal Tutor in 1948 and stayed for over three years. Her nursing had commenced in Birmingham as she did *"her gynae-*

cological training at the Women's' Hospital" before doing her general training at Kings' College Hospital London in the 1930's. Miss Bomford was remembered for having *'a lovely sense of humour'* and it was noted that *'she always looked immaculate in her uniform'*.

Her teaching was of the highest standard, but almost as important were the wonderful influences she managed to transmit. She left QEH and nurse teaching in 1951 to pursue a career in nurse administration for some 19 years, mostly spent as Matron of St. Helier's Hospital Carshalton.

After years of retirement and because of illness, Miss Bomford had to move from her home to a nursing home; this proved a great wrench and it was at this time that a QEHNL member began to visit her quite regularly. These visits grew in importance, were greatly appreciated by an 'alert spruce Sister Tutor' and a mutual bond developed. When her will dated March 1986 was proven, the League read:

> *"I give devise and bequeath all the rest and residue of my estate . . . to divide my Residuary Estate into 62 equal parts and pay the same as follows:-*
>
> *(a) As to 8 parts to King's College Hospital Nurses League . . . to be utilised by the Executive Committee*
> *(b) As to 4 parts to Queen Elizabeth Hospital Nurses League . . . to be utilised by the Executive Committee.*

Thus it was that the QEHNL received £6821.41 from this kind and generous lady. It is this legacy, and others that followed, that gave the League the financial security that supported the development of this book. Consequently it is with great pleasure that the QEH Nurses League are able to acknowledge this bequest in such a public way.

Conclusion

This chapter has focused on just a few of the very talented women who took a lead role in developing nursing in the Queen Elizabeth Hospital during the early years. The editing team recognise that there are many they more that could be acknowledged for their roles in nursing in the QEH but space did not permit this. The importance of the collective contribution of many individuals to nursing developments by many very able and talented nurses is well recognised and, in singling out a few we hope to reflect the commitment to their profession demonstrated by nurses during the time period covered by this book.

Conclusion

It has been said that a hospital cannot escape from caring for the sick, but it chooses to educate its nurses. The alumni of the Queen Elizabeth Hospital School of Nursing believe that they were well educated and that the core of that education was exemplified by the motto. "To heal; to teach; to learn". (The motto of the United Birmingham Hospitals). Members of the QEHNL were keen to recount their stories of learning and healing, in the teaching environment created at the QEH in the years of the first training school in 1938 to the last group that entered this school in 1957.

The stories told in this book are the memories of some of the nurses who trained and worked at the QEH during the years of 1938 to 1957. It draws largely on the recollections of members of the QE Hospital Nurses League which is comprised of nurses who trained and worked in the QEH during those years. The fact that the League continues to be supported, with a membership of over 550 is a strong tribute to the strength of friendships forged during nurse training and shared experiences in nursing at the QEH. No doubt these friendships were sealed by the support each student nurse or member of the nursing staff was able to give to colleagues during the 'hard times encountered' and the camaraderie developed during the good times.

The Queen Elizabeth Hospital (QEH) continues to thrive and serve the community today and, as this book goes to press, it is part of the University Hospital NHS Trust with Selly Oak Hospital. Many of the features of the building described in this book can still be seen although in recent years there have been a number of developments that have changed the layout of wards areas and some parts of the hospital. Nursing too has changed and, perhaps, the most apt way of summarising this is drawing on the notion of the 'past as a different country, they do things differently there'[1]. It is because of these differences that the members of the Queen Elizabeth Hospital Nurses League were keen to tell their story. Whilst many nurses who trained and worked in the time span identified, (and indeed before and after), will relate to aspects of nurse training and care discussed in this book. The experience of nursing at the new QEH was made unique by the world events at the time and the investments in the ideas leading to the creation of a visionary building and training centre. However, most importantly it was the people that made it all happen, the leaders and colleagues that influenced and supported these nurses in their work. It is to them that the final acknowledgement should be made.

[1] LP Hartley The Go Between

REFERENCES

BALLARD Phillida (1985)   'A City at War' B'ham 1939–45 B'ham Museum Art Gallery'

BARNES Stanley   The Birmingham Hospitals Centre (1952) Stamford and Mann, Birmingham

BARRINGER Floyd S.   Wartime Odyssey. 11th July, 1944, 307

BARRINGER Floyd S.   Wartime Odyssey – 8th – 26th June, 1944. 298–305

BIFFEN nee Thomas Joyce   1938 Letters
News from Nurses League QEH 1991

BIRMINGHAM EVENING MAIL   Quotation 26th September 1944 in Wartime Odyssey – F. S. Barringer

BIRMINGHAM EVENING MAIL   Quotation 13th July 1988 in News from Nurses League QEH 1988

CHAND nee Spencer May   QEH 50 years ago. A personal story. News from Nurses League QEH 1990

DAVIES Ben   Summary of talk – League Day 1990 News from Nurses League QEH 1991

DEBENHAM Robert K.   The Wartime Diary of R.K. Debenham 1939–45 Mar.45

DENT nee Woodhouse Elizabeth   Personal letter to Doreen Tennant 1974

HAYES nee Weston Dawn   Memories of 1939–1944 in QEH News from Nurses League QEH 1989 19–20

LERWILL Joan   Letter from Bournemouth News from Nurses League QEH 1988 39

Plus references taken from:
"The Hospital" 1933–1939 – Journal of the Incorporated Association of Hospital Officers.
Reports of the Board of Governors of the Birmingham United Hospitals

Extracts from the 'News from the Nurses League' (Queen Elizabeh Hospital Nurses League Magazine)

APPENDICES

QEHNTS PTS intakes

The details of all intakes in the time span covered by this text, that is the time period of the Queen Elizabeth Nurse Training School, can be found in Figure below. It should be noted that the first male nurse were recorded as entering the programme with the 25 PTS.

Details of P.T.S. Numbers 1–68 Queen Elizabeth Hospital Nurse Training School

P.T.S	Date Commenced	No Arrived	No Qualified	No Left	% Left	Comments
1st	04.10.38	34	24	10	29	
2nd	17.01.39	18	15	3	16.5	
3rd	18.04.39	15	9	6	40	
4th	05.09.39	28	17	11	40.5	
5th	03.01.40	39	24	15	38	
6th	02.04.40	18	9	9	50	
7th	03.09.40	39	24	15	38	
8th	07.01.41	20	10	10	50	
9th	22.04.41	19	12	7	36.5	
10th	02.09.41	37	30	7	19	
11th	06.01.42	27	19	8	29.5	
12th	14.04.42	26	11	12	57.5	
13th	08.09.42	41	30	11	27	
14th	05.01.43	40	23	17	42.5	
15th	13.04.43	37	24	13	35	
16th	14.09.43	40	25	15	37.5	

17th	04.01.44	41	21	20	48.5	
18th	18.04.44	38	22	16	42.5	
19th	05.09.44	43	26	17	39.5	
20th	09.01.45	41	27	14	34	
21st	09.04.45	42	25	17	40	
22nd	04.09.45	40	28	12	30	
23rd	08.01.46	40	25	15	37.5	
24th	30.04.46	39	25	14	35.5	
25th	03.09.46	39	27	12	30.5	3M/N 2 left pre-SRN 1 SRN Nov 1949
26th	07.01.47	40	24	16	40	2 M/N – 1 left pre-SRN 1 – (had RMPA) awarded SRN March 1950
27th	25.02.47	39	28	11	28	1M/N SRN
28th	15.04.47	34	23	11	32	1 M/N – left pre SRN
29th	26.08.47	37	21	16	43	2 M/N – 1 left pre SRN 1 – (had RMPA) SRN July 1950
30th	20.01.48	37	28	9	24	2 M/N – 1 left pre SRN 1 – SRN
31st	06.04.48	38	29	10	26	1 M/N – left pre SRN
32nd	16.04.48	36	27	9	25	1 M/N – SRN Nov 1951
33th	26.10.48	35	24	11	31	
34th	04.01.49	36	26	10	27.5	1 M/N – left pre SRN
35th	29.03.49	37	25	12	32	1 M/N – left pre SRN
36th	12.07.49	36	25	11	30.5	
37th	03.10.49	36	26	10	27.5	1 M/N – left pre SRN
38th	02.01.50	36	31	5	14	
39th	04.04.50	39	33	6	15	2 M/N – left pre SRN 1 – SRN July 1953
40th	18.07.50	37	26	11	29.5	1M/N SRN Nov 1953
41st	10.10.50	38	28	10	26	1 M/N – left after 7 days

42nd	02.01.51	34	25	9	26	
43rd	03.04.51	38	31	7	18	2 M/N – SRN Nov 1954 -
44th	16.07.51	36	25	11	30.5	
45th	09.10.51	39	28	11	28	2 M/N – 2 left pre SRN
46th	01.01.52	36	29	7	19.5	
47th	01.04.52	38	35	3	8	
48th	15.07.52	38	27	11	29	
49th	07.10.52	38	30	8	21	1 M/N – **John Jeffrey WOOD** SRN Nov 1955
50th	06.01.53	39	29	10	25.5	
51st	31.03.53	41	30	11	26.5	
52nd	05.10.53	34	31	3	8.5	
53rd	05.01.54	39	17	12	30.5	1 M/N – SRN Noc 1956
54th	30.03.54	38	27	11	29	1 M/N SRN July 1957
55th	30.03.54	37	25	12	32	
56th	13.07.54	37	28	9	24	
57th	05.10.54	40	31	9	22.5	1 M/N – left pre SRN
58th	04.01.55	38	34	4	10.5	
59th	28.03.55	38	31	7	18	
60th	12.07.55	38	28	10	26	
61st	04.10.55	39	28	11	28	
62nd	10.01.56	37	32	5	13.5	
63rd	04.04.56	39	29	10	25.5	
64th	17.07.56	39	33	6	15	
65th	09.10.56	38	33	5	13	
66th	08.01.57	41	37	4	9.5	
67th	02.04.57	38	30	8	21	1 M/N – left pre SRN
68th	16.07.57	37	31	7	19	

HOUSE COMMITTEE
OF THE QUEEN ELIZABETH HOSPITAL
United Birmingham Hospitals

June, 1953

T. A. HAMILTON BAYNES, M.A., F.C.A., J.P. (*Chairman*).

A. L. D'ABREU, *O.B.E.*, M.B., Ch.M., F.R.C.S., L.R.C.P.

C. BATCHELOR.

MRS. J. C. BURMAN.

ALDERMAN W. L. DINGLEY.

J. G. EMANUEL, B.Sc., M.D., F.R.C.P.

C. A. F. HASTILOW, *O.B.E.*, M.Sc., B.Com.

F. SELBY TAIT, M.B., Ch.B., F.R.C.S.

A. SHANKS, *M.C.*

ERIC W. VINCENT.

The following, being members of the Board of Governors of the United Birmingham Hospitals, are ex-officio members of the House Committee.

The Chairman of the Board of Governors	EVAN AG NORTON, M.A.
The Chairman of the Finance Committee	KEITH MINDELSOHN, B.A.
The Chairman of the Establishment Committee	W. J. SIMPSON.
The Chairman of the Nursing and Midwifery Committee	MRS. B. L. S. MURTAGH.
The Chairman of the Medical Advisory Committee	PROFESSOR J. M. SMELLIE, *O.B.E.*, M.D., F.R.C.P.

OFFICERS OF THE HOSPITAL
CONSULTANT OFFICERS
(Honoris Causa)

Physicians :

J. G. EMANUEL, M.D., B.Sc., F.R.C.P.
A. STANLEY BARNES, M.D., D.Sc., LL.D., F.R.C.P.
EMERITUS PROFESSOR W. H. WYNN, M.D., B.Sc. (Lond.) M.Sc. (Birm.) F.R.C.P.
G. EDEN, B.A., M.D., F.R.C.P.
A. V. NEALE, M.D., F.R.C.P., D.P.H.
T. L. HARDY, M.A., M.D., F.R.C.P. (*Professor of Gastroenterology*).

Surgeons :

EMERITUS PROFESSOR L. P. GAMGEE, Ch.M., F.R.C.S.
FRANK BARNES, M.B., M.S., F.R.C.S.
EMERITUS PROFESSOR SEYMOUR C. BARLING, *C.M.G.*, M.B., M.S., Ch.M., F.R.C.S.
H. H. SAMPSON, *O.B.E.*, *M.C.*, F.R.C.S.

Obstetrician and Gynaecologist :

LEWIS GRAHAM, M.S., F.R.C.S.

Surgeon to the Throat and Ear Department :

E. MUSGRAVE WOODMAN, M.B., M.S., F.R.C.S.

Anaesthetist :

G. W. HASSALL, L.M.S.S.A.

Radiologist :

HAROLD BLACK, M.D., F.R.C.P., F.F.R., D.P.H.

CONSULTANT OFFICERS

* *Signifies whole-time Officers of the University of Birmingham holding appointments with the United Birmingham Hospitals.*

Physicians :

P. C. P. CLOAKE, M.D., B.Sc., F.R.C.P., D.P.H., D.P.M. (*Professor of Neurology*).
ERNEST BULMER, *C.B.E.*, *T.D.*, Legion of Merit, M.D., F.R.C.P. (Edin. & Eng.).
O. BRENNER, M.D., F.R.C.P.
A. BRIAN TAYLOR, M.D., F.R.C.P.
C. R. ST. JOHNSTON, M.D., F.R.C.P.
*W. MELVILLE ARNOTT, *T.D.*, M.D., B.Sc., F.R.C.P. (Edin. & Eng.). (*William Withering Professor of Medicine*).
*W. TREVOR COOKE, M.A., M.D., F.R.C.P. (*First Assistant in the Dept. of Medicine*).
G. E. O. WILLIAMS, M.D., M.R.C.P.
A. G. W. WHITFIELD, M.D., M.R.C.P.
*K. W. DONALD, *D.S.C.*, M.A., M.D., F.R.C.P.
P. H. DAVISON, M.D., M.R.C.P.

Paediatrician :

JAMES M. SMELLIE, *O.B.E.*, *T.D.*, M.D., F.R.C.P. (*Professor of Paediatrics and Child Health*).

Surgeons :	R. P. SCOTT MASON, *M.C.*, F.R.C.S.
	*F. A. R. STAMMERS, *C.B.E.*, *T.D.*, B.Sc., M.B., Ch.M., F.R.C.S. (*Professor of Surgery*).
	R. K. DEBENHAM, *C.B.E.*, *T.D.*, M.A., M.D., F.R.C.S.
	FAUSET WELSH, B.Sc., M.B., Ch.B., F.R.C.S.
	A. L. D'ABREU, *O.B.E.*, M.B., Ch.M., F.R.C.S., L.R.C.P.
	J. LEIGH COLLIS, M.D., B.Sc., Ch.B., F.R.C.S.
	G. H. BAINES, M.A., M.B., B.Chir., F.R.C.S.
	*B. N. BROOKE, M.Chir., F.R.C.S. (*First Assistant in the Department of Surgery*).
	*D. M. MORRISSEY, M.Chir., F.R.C.S. (Edin. & Eng.).
	A. GOUREVITCH, *M.C.*, M.B., F.R.C.S.
Surgeon to the Department of Urology :	HUGH DONOVAN, M.B., Ch.B., F.R.C.S. (Edin. & Eng.), L.R.C.P.
Obstetricians and Gynaecologists :	F. SELBY TAIT, M.B., Ch.B., F.R.C.S.
	SAMUEL DAVIDSON, *A.F.C.*, M.B., Ch.B., F.R.C.S. (Edin.), F.R.C.O.G.
	*HUGH C. MCLAREN, M.D., F.R.F.P.S.G., F.R.C.S. (Edin.), F.R.C.O.G., (*Professor of Obstetrics and Gynaecology*).
	*M. J. D. NOBLE, M.B., Ch.B., F.R.C.S. (Edin.), M.R.C.O.G. (*First Assistant in the Department of Obstetrics and Gynaecology*).
Surgeons to the Throat and Ear Department :	W. STIRK ADAMS, M.B., Ch.B., M.R.C.S., L.R.C.P., F.R.C.S.
	R. REGINALD S. STRANG, M.B., Ch.B., F.R.C.S., D.L.O.
	N. L. CRABTREE, M.B., Ch.B., F.R.C.S., D.L.O.
Ophthalmic Surgeons:	C. RUDD, M.B., Ch.B., F.R.F.P.S.G., D.O.M.S.
	P. JAMESON EVANS, M.A., B.Ch., M.D., F.R.C.S., D.O.M.S.
Dental Surgeons :	R. O. WALKER, F.D.S., R.C.S. (Eng.), L.R.C.P. and S., H.D.D., L.D.S.R.C.S. (Edin.).
	R. F. PUSEY, B.D.S., M.R.C.S., L.R.C.P.
Physicians to the Neurological Department :	P. C. P. CLOAKE, M.D., B.Sc., F.R.C.P., D.P.H., D.P.M. (*Professor of Neurology*).
	GILBERT S. HALL, M.D., F.R.C.P.
	*J. M. JEFFERSON, M.A., B.Sc., B.M., M.R.C.P. (*First Assistant in the Department of Neurology*).
Surgeons to the Department of Neuro-Surgery :	E. BRODIE HUGHES, Ch.M., M.B., B.S., F.R.C.S. (*Professor of Neuro-Surgery*).
	J. M. SMALL, M.B., Ch.B., F.R.C.S.
	E. A. TURNER, M.B., Ch.B., F.R.C.S.
Plastic Surgeon :	OLIVER T. MANSFIELD, F.R.C.S., L.R.C.P.
Psychiatrists :	MYRE SIM, M.D. (Edin.), D.P.M.
	R. W. TIBBETTS, M.A., B.M., B.Ch., D.P.M.
Anaesthetists :	H. W. FEATHERSTONE, *O.B.E.*, *T.D.*, LL.D., M.A., M.D. B.Chir., F.F.A.R.C.S., D.A.
	L. T. CLARKE, *T.D.*, B.Sc., M.B., Ch.B., M.R.C.S., L.R.C.P., F.F.A.R.C.S., D.A.
	B. L. S. MURTAGH, M.B., Ch.B., M.R.C.S., L.R.C.P., F.F.A.R.C.S., D.A.
	MARION W. S. GREEN, M.B., Ch.B., D.A.
	G. A. RAWLINS, *D.S.C.*, M.B., D.A.
	J. W. WOODWARD, M.B., Ch.B., D.A.
Radiologists :	C. G. TEALL, M.D., F.F.R.
	J. F. BRAILSFORD, M.D., Ph.D., F.I.C.S., F.R.C.P., F.F.R., F.S.R.
	OLIVER E. SMITH, M.B., Ch.B., D.M.R.D., F.F.R.
	J. F. K. HUTTON, M.B., Ch.B., D.M.R.D.
Physicians to the Skin Department :	BERNARD C. TATE, *M.B.E.*, M.A., M.D., F.R.C.P.
	E. BAYLIS ASH, M.B., M.R.C.P.
Endocrinologist :	A. C. CROOKE, M.A., M.D., B.Chir.
Department of Clinical Pathology :	A. L. P. PEENEY, M.R.C.S., L.R.C.P. (*Director of Clinical Pathological Services*).
Radiotherapists to the Department of Radiotherapeutics :	J. F. BROMLEY, *O.B.E.*, M.B., Ch.B., M.R.C.P., D.M.R.E., F.F.R. (*Director*).
	R. MORRISON, M.D., M.R.C.P., (Edin.), F.R.C.S. (Edin.), D.M.R., F.F.R. (*Deputy Director*).
	G. M. HOLME, M.B., Ch.B., D.M.R.T.
	W. H. BOND, M.B., Ch.B., F.R.C.S., D.M.R.T.
Chief Biochemist :	GARFIELD THOMAS, M.Sc., F.R.I.C.
Chief Pharmacist :	E. G. SPEAKMAN, Ph.C.
Principal Physicist :	ANSON QUINTON, M.Sc., A.Inst.P.D.
Principal Almoner :	MISS N. FREW, A.M.I.A.
Principal Physiotherapist :	MISS B. CHATWIN, M.C.S.P.
Secretary and Principal Administrative Officer, United Birmingham Hospitals :	G. A. PHALP, B.Com.
Chief Finance Officer :	D. R. FELTON, A.L.A.A.
Matron :	MISS C. A. SMALDON, S.R.N.
House Governor :	BERNARD SYLVESTER, F.H.A.